CERTIFICATE SCIENCE

FOR NEAB

▪

PHYSICS

K Foulds

JOHN MURRAY

Other titles in this series:
Certificate Science for NEAB Biology ISBN 0 7195 7515 X
Certificate Science for NEAB Chemistry ISBN 0 7195 7514 1
Certificate Science for NEAB Teacher's Resource File ISBN 0 7195 7516 8

GCSE Science Double Award series:
GCSE Science Double Award Biology ISBN 0 7195 7157 X
GCSE Science Double Award Chemistry ISBN 0 7195 7158 8
GCSE Science Double Award Physics ISBN 0 7195 7159 6
GCSE Science Double Award Teacher's Resource File ISBN 0 7195 7246 0

© K Foulds, 1997

First published in 1997
by John Murray (Publishers) Ltd
50 Albemarle Street
London W1X 4BD

Layouts by Eric Drewery
Illustrations by Art Construction, Tom Cross and Linden Artists
Cover design by John Townson/Creation

Typeset in Rockwell Light and News Gothic by
Wearset, Boldon, Tyne & Wear.
Printed and bound in Great Britain by Butler and Tanner Ltd, Frome and London.

A CIP catalogue record for this book is available from the
British Library.

ISBN 0 7195 7513 3

Contents

How to do investigations

Investigations are done in order to collect information that helps us answer questions, test ideas or solve problems.

Imagine seeing this advert. Would you believe the claims made in the advert? After all, there is no evidence to show that the claims have been tested! The only way we could be sure would be to carry out an investigation to test the claim. But what would we be testing?

The first step...

... in any investigation is to make sure you understand what you are testing. Here you would be trying to answer the question:

The second step is to think about how you would collect information to help you answer the question (see *Certificate Science Biology*, page 22 – Planning your investigations). You would have to:

- collect several different brands of battery, and
- measure how long it takes for each battery to go flat.

To help organise your results it is best to have a table ready (see *Certificate Science Chemistry*, page 44 – Designing tables). For these tests the table should have the headings shown below.

Make of battery	How long it lasted
↑	↑

This will show the thing you change during your tests – the make of battery

This will show what you measure as you change from one battery to another – how long each battery lasts before going flat

Having done all that work you don't want anyone claiming that your tests were unfair. To make sure that they were fair (see *Certificate Science Biology*, page 44 – What to do to make your tests 'fair') you would have to:

- choose the same size battery, with the same voltage, from the different manufacturers,
- use each battery in the same circuit, with the same type of bulb each time, and
- make sure all other conditions are the same.

You will want others to see clearly what you have found out. One way to help is to put your results into a graph or chart (see page 20). In this case it will be a bar chart.

Make of battery	How long it lasted
Lastalot	7h 15min
Everbrite	8h 40min
Cheapo	6h 35min
Betterbrands	9h 10min
Starlite	7h 2min

From the bar chart you can see the differences between one battery and another more easily. Now you've got some results you can use them to compare how well each battery lasted. You can see from the chart that some batteries lasted longer than others – *Betterbrands* battery lasted longest, while *Cheapo* lasted the shortest time.

You can now write down what you have found out (see *Certificate Science Chemistry*, page 66 – What do your results mean?). You could say something like:

> Our tests show that some batteries last longer than others (when tested under the same conditions). The <u>Betterbrands</u> battery lasted longest, and the <u>Cheapo</u> battery lasted the shortest time. The <u>Lastalot</u> battery lasted longer than some brands but not as long as others.

Now you have **evidence** (your measurements), you can definitely say that the advert was a load of rubbish!

Finally, you should write a report about what you did. You will find further help on page 66 of *Certificate Science Biology*.

Summary

In an investigation:

- make sure you understand what you are testing or trying to find out,
- think about what you are going to change and what you will measure,
- think about how many measurements you will need to make – sometimes you will need lots of measurements so that you can be sure of what you say,
- plan ahead so that you know what equipment you will need,
- make sure you think about how to make your tests fair,

- organise your results into a table,
- try to show your results on a graph or chart,
- always write a sentence or two at the end saying what the results mean, and, finally,
- check that you have answered the question you set out to test.

You will find information throughout this book to help you whenever you do an investigation – use it to help you produce your best possible work for assessment.

Acknowledgements

Cover *tr* and *main picture* Tony Stone, *remainder* ZEFA; **p.1** Andrew Harrington/ BBC Natural History Unit; **p.3** and **p.5** John Townson/Creation; **p.6** ZEFA; **p.8** *l* Peter Bassett/BBC Natural History Unit, *c* ZEFA, *r* The Hutchison Library; **p.9** *t* Stephen Krasemann/NHPA, *b* Andrew Harrington/BBC Natural History Unit; **p.14** Shout Pictures; **p.15** Jim Amos/Science Photo Library; **p.16** *l* ZEFA, *r* R Maisonneuve, Publiphoto Diffusion/Science Photo Library; **p.17** John Cleare Mountain Camera; **p.18** Martin Bond/Science Photo Library; **p.19** Lowell Georgia/ Science Photo Library; **p.20** and **p.21** Peter Menzel/Science Photo Library; **p.23** and **p.24** Last Resort; **p.27** John Townson/Creation; **p.30** *t* GeoScience Features, *cl* Barnaby's Picture Library, *cr* John Townson/Creation; **p.31** *l* John Townson/Creation, *r* Pifco Ltd; **p.34** *t* Adrienne Hart-Davis/Science Photo Library, *b* Andrew Lambert; **p.35** John Townson/Creation; **p.36** ZEFA; **p.43** Space Telescope Science Institute/NASA/Science Photo Library; **p.46** Sporting Pictures (UK) Ltd; **p.49** *t* J Wakelin/TRIP, *cl* I Hoath/TRIP, *cr* Last Resort; **p.50** *t* Simon Bruty/Allsport UK, *c* Andrew Lambert; **p.52** *cl* John Townson/Creation, *cr* © Wallace & Gromit/Aardman Animations Ltd 1995, *b* GeoScience Features; **p.54** *tl* Science Photo Library, *tr* Last Resort, *cl* Halcrow, *cr* Andrew Lambert, *bl* Alan Carruthers/Science Photo Library, *br* ZEFA; **p.55** J Wakelin/TRIP; **p.56** ZEFA; **p.57** Last Resort; **p.58** QA Photos; **p.60** *l* NASA/Science Photo Library, *r* John Frassanitor, NASA/Science Photo Library; **p.61** *t* Photo Library International/Science Photo Library, *c* John Sanford/Science Photo Library, *bl* ESA/ Science Photo Library, *br* NRSC LTD/Science Photo Library; **p.62** *tl* NASA/Science Photo Library, *tr* Space Telescope Science Institute/NASA/Science Photo Library, *c* and *b* NASA/Science Photo Library; **p.63** US Geological Survey/Science Photo Library; **p.66** *tl* Planet Earth Pictures, *tr* Francois Gohier/Science Photo Library, *b* George East/Science Photo Library; **p.67** NASA/Science Photo Library; **p.69** Science Photo Library; **p.71** ZEFA; **p.72** Rex Features; **p.75** ZEFA; **p.76** *c* Saturn Stills/Science Photo Library, *br* Department of Clinical Radiology, Salisbury District Hospital/Science Photo Library; **p.77** Dentsply UK; **p.78** *tr* Shout Pictures, *cl* ZEFA, *bl* Geoff Tompkinson/Science Photo Library; **p.79** *c* Rex Features, *b* ZEFA; **p.80** ZEFA; **p.83** Francoise Sauze/Science Photo Library; **p.84** ZEFA; **p.85** *l* Sainsbury's, *r* Markitwise International; **p.87** Martin Dohrn/ Science Photo Library

(*t* = top, *b* = bottom, *r* = right, *l* = left, *c* = centre)

The Publishers have made every effort to contact copyright holders. If any have been overlooked they will make the necessary arrangements at the earliest opportunity.

ENERGY

Energy and you

My muscles just won't run any further.

This drink quickly replaces the energy I've used.

Every muscle in your body needs **energy** to work. The energy is released from chemicals in food and drink. Even when you are sitting still you need energy to stay alive and keep you warm. You can see from the table that the more work your muscles have to do, the more energy they need.

Activity	Energy released by the body each minute
Lying in bed	6000 joules
Sitting watching TV	9000 joules
Walking slowly	13 500 joules
Walking quickly	21 000 joules
Running	25 000 joules
Swimming	33 000 joules

The **joule** is the unit of energy (just as the metre is a unit of length). 1 joule (1 J) is a very small amount of energy. That is why amounts of energy often have very large numbers. A bigger unit, the kilojoule (kJ), is often used. 1 kilojoule is the same as 1000 joules.

Where does the energy come from?

Food contains many different chemicals. Inside the body some of the chemicals react with oxygen to release energy during respiration.

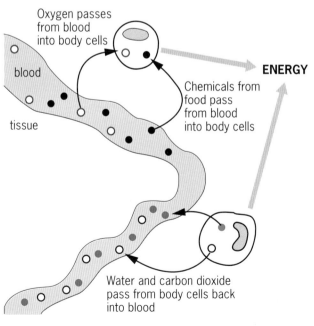

Oxygen passes from blood into body cells

blood

ENERGY

Chemicals from food pass from blood into body cells

tissue

Water and carbon dioxide pass from body cells back into blood

Chemicals from food react with oxygen in the cells of the body, and energy is released

This supplies about 80 000 joules (80 kJ)

This supplies about 1 300 000 joules (1300 kJ)

This supplies about 550 000 joules (550 kJ)

This supplies about 300 000 joules (300 kJ)

The amount of energy released from food depends on:

- how much you eat – the more food you eat, the more energy can be released;
- the kind of food – some foods release more energy than others.

Some people need more energy than others. A road worker, for example, needs more energy than an office worker. Each person should eat enough to provide the energy he or she needs.

The right foods eaten in the right amounts (a balanced diet) provide all the energy (and other nutrients) that the body needs.

★ THINGS TO DO

1 The table shows the energy value of several chocolate bars.

Bar	Energy value
Wispa	880 000 joules
Mars bar	1 234 000 joules
50 g milk chocolate	1 076 000 joules
Twix	1 285 000 joules
Double Decker	953 000 joules

a) Which chocolate bar supplies most energy?
b) Which chocolate bar supplies least energy?
c) Make a bar chart showing the energy value of the chocolate bars.

2 Some elderly people keep warm in winter by wrapping themselves in blankets during the day. Someone suggested that they could try putting a layer of aluminium foil between two blankets. Do you think this would be better at keeping them warm?

Test the idea yourselves. You could use a flask filled with warm water instead of a real person, and dusters (or old clothing) instead of blankets.

Write a report saying what you did and what you found out.

Energy and work

You exert a force which lifts the box, so you do work

You exert a force on the pedals which makes the boat move, so you do work

We use the word 'work' in many ways, such as 'I've been doing my homework', or 'I've been to work'. In science the word work has a special meaning. If something is moving *and* a force is acting on it then **work** is being done.

In the examples above, energy is released in the muscles when work is done. When we say something has energy, we really mean it can exert a force on something and do work on it. There are many different forms of energy.

The battery does work pushing current through the circuit. It is the chemicals in the battery that store the energy needed to do the work. We say the battery has **chemical energy**

Things that are moving can exert forces which make other things move. They can do work. We say that moving objects have **kinetic energy**

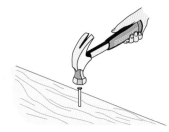

Something that has been lifted above its normal position can exert a force which makes something else move. Here the hammer can do work on the nail, driving it into the wood. We say the hammer has **potential energy**

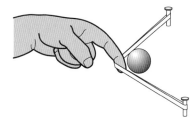

Materials that are stretched (or squashed) can exert forces which make things move. They also have **potential energy**

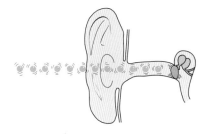

Sound makes particles in the air vibrate. The vibrating air particles make your ear drum move. They do work on your ear drum. We say the air particles have **sound energy**

A power supply pushes current through a circuit and the current does work on the devices in the circuit. The power supply can be thought of as a source of **electrical energy**

What happens to the energy?

In each of the examples shown opposite, energy is passed from place to place, or from one thing to another. Consider the stretched rubber band.

- *Chemical energy* in the muscles lets you do work on the rubber band as you stretch it.
- The stretched band now has *potential energy*.
- When the band is released it pushes on the ball, making it move. The band does *work* on the ball.
- The moving ball has *kinetic energy*.

These energy changes can be written as:

$$\text{chemical energy} \rightarrow \text{potential energy} \rightarrow \text{kinetic energy}$$

Many of the things we use are designed to change energy in a particular way.

These things are designed to bring about energy changes

electrical energy in → sound energy out

electrical energy in → kinetic energy out

In all cases it is important to remember that energy never disappears – it changes from one form into another. In any energy change, some *heat energy* is always produced.

When an electric fire is used, the amount of heat energy from the fire is the same as the amount of electrical energy supplied to it. Energy has not been lost – it has all been changed into a different form.

★ THINGS TO DO

1 Make a big poster showing things that work in your home. You could draw them or cut out pictures from catalogues. For each one add labels showing:

- what kind of energy it needs to work,
- what kind of energy it releases.

2 A group of pupils tested different fuels to find out which released most energy when they were burned. Part of their account is shown on the right.

a) What steps should the pupils have taken to make their test 'fair'?

b) Assuming their test was fair, which fuel released most energy? Explain your answer using their results.

c) One pupil said that 'all of the energy released by the fuel was transferred to the water'. Do you agree? If not, say what you think could have happened to some of the energy released by the fuel.

We put each fuel in a small crucible and burned it so that the heat warmed some water in a beaker above the crucible. We measured the temperature rise of the water for each fuel.

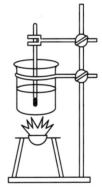

Fuel	Starting temperature of water/°C	Temperature after heating/°C	Rise in temperature/°C
meths	16	57	41
paraffin	17	46	29
meta (solid fuel)	15	57	42

A waste of money

Oil, coal and gas are fuels which release energy when they are burned. These sources of energy are running out. If we waste energy then the oil, gas, and coal will run out faster.

Think about your own home. How often is the television switched on but no one is watching it? How often is there a light on when there is no one in the room? We are all responsible for wasting energy.

Leaving the engine running wastes petrol

Efficiency

Even when we are using things, a lot of energy is usually being wasted.

An electric fire is designed to change electrical energy into heat. A good fire changes *all* of the electrical energy in a useful way – into heat energy. No energy is wasted so the fire is an **efficient** device – 100% efficient.

Other things are less efficient. An 'ordinary' light bulb *should* change electrical energy into light energy. What really happens is quite different!

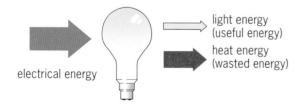

electrical energy

light energy (useful energy)

heat energy (wasted energy)

The light bulb changes most of the electrical energy into heat energy. This is wasted energy because we want light from it. Only about $\frac{1}{5}$ of the electrical energy is changed into light energy. This type of bulb is not very efficient.

Are there people in all of these offices?

A different type of bulb – a *low-energy* bulb – is much more efficient. Although these bulbs are more expensive to buy, they are much cheaper to use. They produce the same brightness as an ordinary bulb, but use less electrical energy.

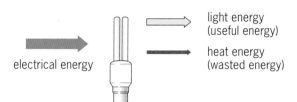

electrical energy

light energy (useful energy)

heat energy (wasted energy)

You can see that the low-energy bulb changes much more of the electrical energy into light energy. Only about $\frac{1}{5}$ is changed into heat (wasted) energy. The bulb is much more efficient than an ordinary bulb because it changes more energy in a useful way. Many schools and offices now use these bulbs, saving hundreds of pounds each year. They also save our energy resources.

By using efficient devices we will:

- reduce the amount of wasted energy,
- help make fuel reserves last longer,
- reduce our fuel bills.

★ THINGS TO DO

1 a) Copy and complete this table showing the way in which energy is changed by each household appliance. The first one has been done for you.

Appliance	Energy change
Electric drill	electrical energy $\Rightarrow$ kinetic energy $\Rightarrow$ sound energy (W) $\Rightarrow$ heat energy (W)
Tumble drier	
Food processor	
Electric kettle	

b) For each one put a W alongside the energy that is effectively wasted energy.
c) Which one do you think wastes most energy?
d) List the appliances in order, with the most efficient at the top and the least efficient at the bottom.
e) How does your list compare with that of a friend? If you disagree, discuss the reasons why you placed them in the order you did. Can you both agree on an order?

2 A car manufacturer made two cars. The only difference was in the shape of the body. Everything else was the same. They then tested the cars on a flat road to find out how far they would run on 1 litre of petrol. These were the results.

Ran for 9 kilometres

Ran for 6 kilometres

a) Which car was most efficient? Why?
b) Try to say why the shape made such a difference.

Temperature

The lowest air temperature recorded on Earth (−89.2 °C) was in Antarctica

The air temperature in the UK on a hot sunny day is about 30 °C

The highest air temperature recorded on Earth (58 °C) was in Libya

When something is heated, energy is passed to it and its **temperature** rises – it gets hotter. Temperature is really just a measure of how hot something is. Temperature is normally measured in degrees Celsius (°C). A temperature of 20 degrees Celsius is written as 20 °C.

Hot or cold?

Temperatures can range from very hot to very cold. The temperature at the surface of the Sun, for example, is about 6000 °C. The surface temperature of Saturn, on the other hand, is about −160 °C. It is so cold because it is so far from the Sun.

On Earth, the air temperature depends on where you are.

Warming up and cooling down

Most of us like hot meals. To warm up food we must supply it with extra energy – using a cooker or a microwave oven. When a gas ring is used to heat soup, the energy from the burning gas passes through the sides of the pan to the soup inside. The soup gets hotter because it gains extra energy.

Energy passes from hotter to cooler regions

Energy spreads from places where the temperature is high to places where the temperature is lower.

If the soup is then poured into a bowl it will begin to cool. The air is at a lower temperature than the soup. Energy passes from the soup to the air (from the hotter region to the cooler region). The soup cools down because it loses energy.

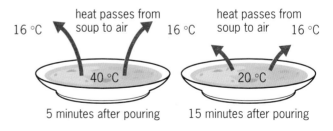

The longer the soup is left to cool, the more energy it loses and the more its temperature falls

Freezing and boiling

If a liquid, such as water, is placed in a freezer, it cools. At 0 °C (the **freezing point** of water) the water freezes and turns to ice. Other liquids freeze at different temperatures.

If water is heated, it gains extra energy and its temperature rises. When the temperature reaches 100 °C (the **boiling point** of water) the water boils, turning rapidly to steam.

In very cold regions of the Earth, sea water freezes forming huge carpets of ice many metres thick

Hot rocks below the Earth's surface heat underground water, changing it to steam

★ THINGS TO DO

1 Sam sells cold drinks on the beach in summer. He puts crushed ice into diluted fruit juice. Some people have complained that the drinks do not stay cold for long and he is losing customers. He thought he would buy different cups. He could try plastic cups *or* polystyrene cups *or* card cups.

Which do you think will work best? Plan and carry out some tests to find out which would be best for Sam. How can you imitate a hot sunny day in your classroom?

Prepare a report when you have finished. Suggest which cup he should use and why.

2 The table below shows the defrosting and cooking times for turkeys of different sizes. The defrosting time assumes the turkey is left in the kitchen.

Size of turkey	Thawing time	Cooking time
2.3–3.6 kg	14–18 hours	2.5–3.25 hours
3.6–5.0 kg	18–24 hours	3.25–3.75 hours
5.0–6.8 kg	24–26 hours	3.75–4.5 hours
6.8–9.0 kg	26–28 hours	4.5–5.0 hours
9.0–11.3 kg	28–36 hours	5.00–5.5 hours

a) What is the connection between the defrosting time and the size of the turkey?
b) Why do smaller turkeys cook faster than larger turkeys?
c) If a turkey is not cooked for long enough, bacteria could survive in the parts that are not fully cooked. Which part of the turkey is most likely to be undercooked?
d) You have bought a frozen turkey which has the label 5.5 kg on the wrapper. How long should you defrost the turkey for? How long should it be cooked for?
e) When the turkey is taken from the freezer its temperature is −8 °C. It is left in the kitchen where the air is at 20 °C. Why does the turkey defrost?

Heat energy on the move

Conduction

During a really cold winter the water in pipes can freeze and split them. When the ice thaws (melts), water escapes from the pipe and floods the house.

The water in the pipes cools down because energy passes from the warmer water in the pipe to the cooler surroundings. The energy is passed through the material of the pipe, from atom to atom by **conduction**. The atoms themselves do not move during the process of heat transfer – they are held in place by the other atoms around them.

Heat passes through metals (such as copper pipes) much more quickly than it does through plastics. That is why the water in copper pipes cools down much more quickly than it does in plastic pipes.

Materials through which energy passes quickly are described as good **conductors**. Most metals are good conductors because they contain electrons that are free to move through the material. These electrons spread the energy much faster than it could be passed from atom to atom.

The water in plastic pipes cools down more slowly because plastics are **insulators**. Energy is conducted slowly through insulators. Most non-metals are insulators. By wrapping the pipe in other insulating materials (such as polystyrene or foam rubber) we can slow down even more the rate at which energy is lost. That may stop the water freezing.

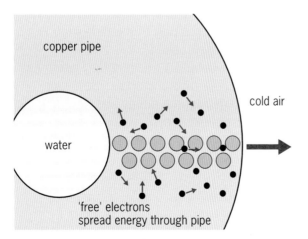

Heat is lost quickly from the water in a copper pipe

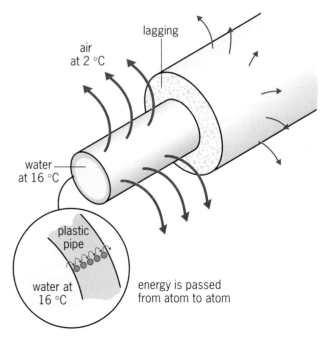

The lagging reduces the rate of heat loss

Convection

Energy can also spread from place to place by **convection**. In an electric kettle the element becomes very hot. This heats the water around it. The warmed water then rises, carrying energy with it. Cooler water moves in around the element, and is in turn heated. It then rises, and the energy becomes spread through the water. When the water reaches 100 °C (the boiling point) it boils.

Convection spreads the heat from hotter regions to cooler regions by the movement of the particles. The particles carry the energy with them as they move around.

A hot drink is cooled (partly) by convection currents. The air above the surface of a hot drink is warmed. The warm air rises, carrying the energy with it. As the drink has lost energy, its temperature falls. Some heat is also lost by **evaporation** as water vapour leaves the surface of the drink.

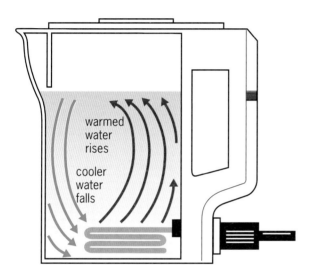

warmed water rises

cooler water falls

The water in a kettle is heated by convection

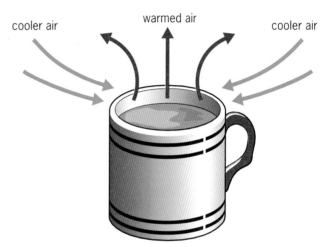

cooler air   warmed air   cooler air

Convection can also cause cooling

★ THINGS TO DO

1 Hill walkers may suffer from hypothermia – loss of body heat. If their temperature falls too quickly they could die. They must be kept warm.

   Plan a test you could do to find out the answers to these questions.

- Do extra layers of clothing really help to keep someone warm for longer?
- If you covered someone (e.g. with a tent) does it help the person stay warm for longer?

What could you use to represent the person, the clothing and the tent? How could you create a cooling 'wind', just like the outdoors, in the classroom/laboratory?

2 The drink in this cup will cool down because it loses heat by conduction and convection.

a) Where does it lose heat by conduction?
b) Where does it lose heat by convection?
c) What could you do to keep the drink warm for a longer time?

Keeping things warm

When our homes are warm we feel comfortable

If the inside is warmer than the outside, energy is lost. We must keep the heating on to stop the house cooling down

We spend lots of money heating our homes so that we can feel comfortable. Sadly, all of the heat energy escapes from the warmer house to the colder surroundings through the walls, windows, floors and roof.

To make up for the energy that is lost in winter, we must keep the heating on. If we cut down the rate at which energy is lost, our homes would stay warm for longer. We would not need to supply as much energy from the heating system, so we would save money and help make fuels last longer.

Cutting the waste

Most of the energy is lost from our homes through the roof and walls. The rate at which energy is lost can be reduced if we insulate our homes well.

- Energy losses from the roof can be reduced using loft insulation.
- Energy losses from the walls can be reduced by putting wall insulation between the inner and outer walls.
- Energy losses from the windows can be reduced by fitting double-glazing. The air space between the panes of glass acts as an insulator.
- Draught excluders can be used to stop cold air entering through the gaps around windows and doors.
- Energy loss through the floor can be reduced by laying fitted carpets.

If all 5 methods of home insulation are used, then the heat loss can be reduced by almost 80%. That means your bills would be only $\frac{1}{5}$ of what they were – and only $\frac{1}{5}$ of the fuel would be needed.

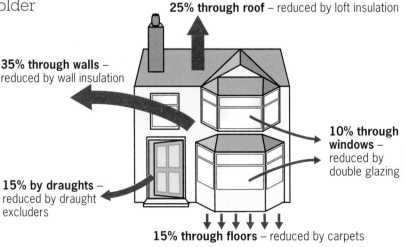

25% through roof – reduced by loft insulation

35% through walls – reduced by wall insulation

10% through windows – reduced by double glazing

15% by draughts – reduced by draught excluders

15% through floors – reduced by carpets

Energy loss from our homes and how to reduce it

Keeping things cool

Insulation is also used to keep things cool. A 'cool bag', for example, is used to keep food and drinks cool when outdoors in summer. If an ordinary bag were used, energy would pass quickly from the warmer air to the cooler contents of the bag, warming them.

Insulating material placed between the outer and inner walls of the cool bag slows down the rate at which energy passes into the bag. The inside does not warm up as quickly, so the contents stay cool for longer.

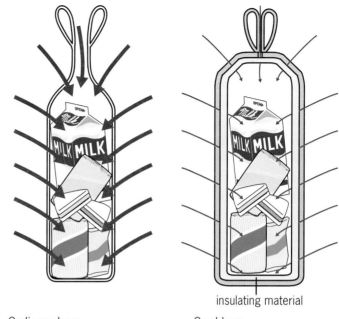

insulating material

Ordinary bag   Cool bag

★ THINGS TO DO

1 This table shows how much it might cost to put different types of insulation in your home. The third column shows how much money would be saved each year from an average heating bill.

Type of insulation	Cost of insulation/£	How much would be saved each year/£
Lagging hot water tank	10	13
Lagging hot water pipes	10	6
Draught-proofing	15	15
Loft insulation	110	60
Wall insulation	600	25
Secondary double-glazing	1200	40

a) Which form of insulation would save the most money each year?

b) Which form seems to be the least worthwhile, considering its cost?

c) Use a calculator to work out:

i) how much it would cost to put loft insulation, wall insulation and draught-proofing into a house;

ii) how much would be saved each year if they were fitted.

d) Which of the methods listed reduces energy losses by *conduction*?

2 Design a leaflet for householders that would encourage them to put insulation in their homes. Point out how much energy is lost from each part of the house, and how much money they could save by putting in some form of insulation.

3 Mr Brown thought that he could insulate his water tank using sheets of polystyrene. He wasn't sure whether the thickness of the polystyrene would affect how much heat would be lost.

Do some tests to find out how the thickness of polystyrene affects the rate of energy loss. Make sure your tests are fair.

Heat waves

When you stand close to a fire you can feel the heat. Energy is being carried to you by 'heat waves', or **radiation**. Some of the radiation is absorbed ('soaked up') by your clothes and you feel warmer.

Just like conduction and convection, radiation transfers energy from place to place. 'Heat waves', however, do not need particles to carry them – they can travel through empty space (a vacuum).

The 'heat waves' are really **electromagnetic waves**. There are many different types of electromagnetic waves (see Unit 4.5). Those given off (radiated) by hot objects – up to a temperature of a few hundred degrees – are called **infra-red** waves, or infra-red radiation.

Everything gives off infra-red radiation, even you. The hotter something is, the more infra-red radiation it gives off.

Police helicopters carry special cameras that allow them to 'see' even in the dark. The cameras detect infra-red radiation from things on the ground. The human body is at a higher temperature than the surroundings so it gives off more infra-red radiation. This is shown up clearly by the camera.

It is mostly infra-red radiation that warms you by a fire, and that toasts bread in a toaster. In a toaster the radiation carries energy from the hot elements to the bread. The radiation is absorbed by the bread, heating the surface.

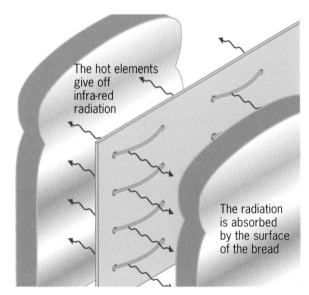

The hot elements give off infra-red radiation

The radiation is absorbed by the surface of the bread

The bread in a toaster gets hotter because it gains energy from the radiation absorbed

Infra-red radiation shows up the suspect even at night

Keeping warm

Babies that are born prematurely must be kept warm at all costs. They may be wrapped in shiny foil and placed in an incubator. The incubator helps reduce energy loss from the baby's body by conduction and evaporation. The shiny foil helps reduce energy loss from the body by radiation.

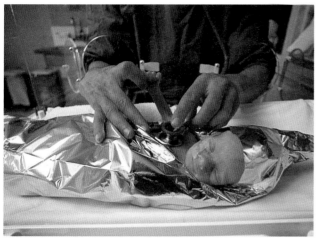

Premature babies must be kept warm

coal fires, there was plenty of soot from the chimneys. Some gardeners used to collect the soot and dig it into the soil. That made the soil darker. The dark soil absorbed more of the Sun's radiation, so the soil warmed faster. Their plants started to grow earlier.

Dark surfaces absorb infra-red radiation better than light-coloured surfaces. They also emit (give off) more infra-red radiation than light surfaces at the same temperature.

Shiny materials reflect infra-red radiation. Rather than escaping into the air, the radiation is reflected back onto the baby's body. Some of it is re-absorbed by the body, helping to keep it warm.

All light, shiny surfaces are good reflectors (poor absorbers) of infra-red radiation. They are also poor emitters (givers-off) of infra-red radiation.

Old gardening tricks

Gardeners know that their seeds germinate faster in warm soil than in cold soil. Years ago, when most people had

★ THINGS TO DO

1 Try to use the words *conduction, convection* or *radiation* in your answers to these questions.
a) Why do you think cricketers sometimes put white cream on their faces?
b) During the hot summer of 1995 the penguins at London Zoo spent more time in the water than usual. Can you think of a reason for this?
c) Seeds germinate faster in warm soil. During springtime many gardeners cover their soil with black plastic sheets. Why do they do this?

2 Barbecues are great fun, but why do the baked potatoes always go cold? Three young people suggested how baked potatoes could be kept warm:
- Daniel said 'wrap them in cooking foil';
- Sheila said 'wrap them in cooking foil then 2 or 3 sheets of paper';
- Anne said 'wrap them in bubble plastic'.

Plan some tests to find out whose method would keep the potatoes warm for longest. Your teacher may let you do the tests and write a report telling others what to do.

Add a section to your report saying how the wrapping affects conduction, convection and radiation.

Fuels

Oil is the source of energy that allows us to transport people and food around the world

Modern manufacturing industries need electricity to power robotic systems

This petrol station sells diesel as well as leaded and unleaded petrol. When these fuels are burned in oxygen they release the energy needed by cars, motorbikes, lorries and buses. All of these fuels are made from oil. Aeroplane and ship fuels also come from oil.

Our homes, offices and manufacturing industries need electricity. Electricity is made in generating (power) stations, most of which use coal, gas, oil or nuclear fuels. These are the sources of the energy needed to generate electricity.

Fossil fuels

Coal, oil and gas are called **fossil fuels** because they formed from the (fossilised) remains of living things such as marine animals and plants.

Coal is a rock formed over thousands of years from the partly decayed remains of plants. The coal is often found hundreds of metres below the surface of the Earth. Eventually we will run out of coal – we will have used it all.

Oil and gas are found trapped between layers of rock well below the surface of the Earth. Bore holes are drilled into the Earth to reach the pockets of gas and oil. Eventually we will run out of oil and gas – we will have emptied all the oil and gas pockets in the Earth.

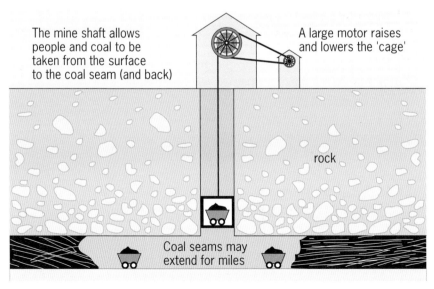

The mine shaft allows people and coal to be taken from the surface to the coal seam (and back)

A large motor raises and lowers the 'cage'

rock

Coal seams may extend for miles

Mine shafts are drilled into the Earth to reach the coal seams (layers of coal)

Burning fossil fuels

When fossil fuels are burned, other 'waste' materials such as carbon dioxide gas and 'soot' are produced.

fuel + oxygen → heat + waste materials

Once burned, fossil fuels cannot be used again. They are called **non-renewable sources** of energy. We can make them last longer by making sure that we do not waste the precious little that is left.

Nuclear fuels

Nuclear power stations use nuclear fuels such as uranium as the source of energy needed to make electricity. Uranium is obtained from the Earth's crust. Inside the core of a nuclear reactor the uranium is bombarded by small particles called neutrons. Some of the uranium atoms split up, releasing energy.

Nuclear fuels release huge amounts of energy. In fact 1 teaspoonful of uranium provides about the same amount of energy as 1 tonne of coal.

The uranium and plutonium used in power stations must be replaced regularly. Eventually the supply of these materials will run out (although coal, oil and gas will run out long before). Nuclear fuels are also **non-renewable sources** of energy.

Wood

Although it might seem that there is an endless supply of wood, if we chop it down faster than it grows it will eventually run out. But if we manage the use of wood carefully, we can make sure that there will be good supplies for the future. In this sense we can think of wood as a **renewable source** of energy.

There are still millions of people in the world who depend on wood for heat

★ THINGS TO DO

1 Use your research skills to find out how coal is formed. Draw a strip cartoon. The first picture should show lots of trees and swampy ground millions of years ago. The final picture should show coal being mined today. Add short captions describing what is going on in each picture.

2 Some camping stoves use a solid chemical called Meta fuel. Others use gas, such as Camping Gaz.

Climbers often argue about which type of fuel boils their water faster. Some say Meta is faster. Others claim Gaz is faster.

Plan and carry out some tests to settle their arguments once and for all. Find out which fuel boils water faster.

Prepare a letter to an outdoor pursuits magazine, describing your tests. Use your results to show which fuel is better.

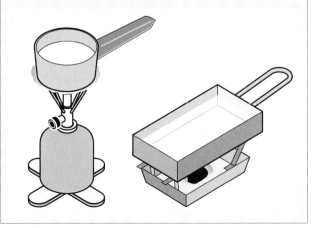

Thinking ahead

Fossil fuels are running out so we must try to find other ways of supplying the energy we will need in the future. Most of the alternatives to fossil fuels are **renewable sources** of energy because they can be used over and over.

Wind energy

Wind turbines like the one shown here are used to generate electricity. There is no pollution from wind generators, but the problem is they cannot generate electricity if there is no wind. Wind generators could not produce all of the electricity we need. They are also expensive.

Hydroelectricity

In hydroelectric systems water is trapped in a lake or reservoir behind a large dam. As the water runs through a pipe in the dam it turns a turbine. This turns a generator which produces the electricity.

Hydroelectricity is a clean, renewable source of energy. The lakes that form behind the dam can be used for leisure such as boating, fishing and windsurfing. They also provide habitats for animals. Some people are against hydroelectric schemes because of the need to flood land.

Generating electricity from the wind

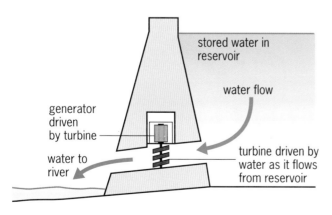

Generating electricity from water

Hydroelectric schemes can only be used in mountainous areas such as Scotland and Wales, which also have the necessary high rainfall.

Solar power

The small solar cells in calculators use the Sun's energy to drive a current through a circuit. More powerful solar cells are now used to power small cars and even light aeroplanes. Satellites use solar cells to power their equipment.

In some parts of the world, sunlight is used to heat large furnaces. The heat is used to produce high-pressure steam, which turns generators in a power station.

Solar furnaces are expensive to build but are a clean source of energy. They need lots of sunshine to be effective so they are not likely to be used in the UK!

Mirrors reflect the sunlight which is absorbed inside the furnace, raising the temperature to over 3000 °C

★ THINGS TO DO

1 Sort the energy sources below into two groups:

- one group of renewable sources,
- one group of non-renewable sources.

coal, nuclear, solar, gas, wind, oil, water (hydroelectric)

2 Two wind generators are being tested on a windy hill. The graphs below show the power produced by each one at different wind speeds.

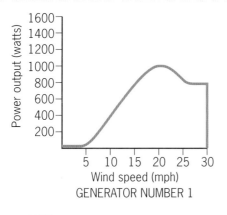
GENERATOR NUMBER 1

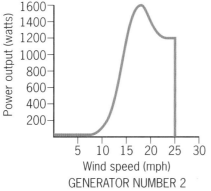
GENERATOR NUMBER 2

a) Copy and complete this table by reading the missing values from the graphs.

Wind speed /mph	Power output	
	generator 1	generator 2
10		
15		
	1000	1400
30		

b) The generators are designed to stop if the wind becomes too strong. At what wind speed did generator number 1 stop working?
c) What wind speed was needed for generator number 2 to start producing electricity?
d) Which generator produced the highest power?

3 Prepare a talk for the rest of your class about solar power *or* wind energy *or* hydroelectricity. Decide who in the class is going to talk about each one. To help the class understand your talk:

- prepare a short leaflet that they can stick in their books. The leaflet should say how the source of energy works, and whether there are any disadvantages in using it; *or*
- use a poster or overhead projector to help them understand what you say; *or*
- use pictures, such as photographs or slides or a section of video film.

Bar charts or line graphs?

Putting the results of your investigations into a chart or a graph can help you to see any connections more easily. It also lets others see what you have found out.

But when should you use a bar chart and when should you use a line graph? Think about the results in these tables.

We tested different cups to find out which was best at keeping drinks warm.

Type of cup	Temperature fall in 10 minutes/°C
plastic	27
polystyrene	18

If the thing you changed can only be described in words (e.g. the type of cup), then your results should go in a bar chart.

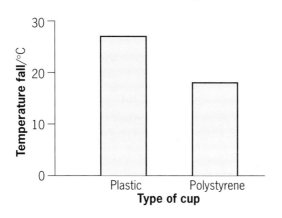

See how to draw bar charts on page 42.

We wrapped different thicknesses of a material around a teapot of hot tea.

Thickness/mm	Temperature fall in 20 minutes/°C
10	37
15	28
20	21
25	17
30	14

If the thing you changed is described by numbers (it could be measured in some way), then you should use a line graph.

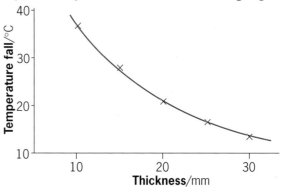

See how to draw line graphs on page 70.

★ THINGS TO DO

Draw a bar chart or a line graph for the results below. You must decide whether to use a bar chart or a line graph each time.

1 We measured the amount of bubbles made by 3 different types of bubble bath.

Type of bubble bath	Height of bubbles/cm
Mr Bubbles	5
Foamalot	8
Peachy	12

2 We measured how high a golf ball bounced when it was dropped from different heights.

How high it was when we dropped it/cm	How high it bounced/cm
10	7
20	15
30	26
40	33
50	41

2

ELECTRICITY

What a shock!

People have known about the effects of static electricity for thousands of years. The Greeks knew that jewellery made from amber (a golden yellow fossilised sap) attracted dust and other materials when it was polished with a cloth.

Later people used electricity for fun. Small boys were fastened to silk ropes and hung above the ground. When they were rubbed with a dry duster their hair stood on end and sometimes sparks jumped from them to people standing nearby – what a shock they got!

Now we can produce similar (but much more dramatic) effects using a van de Graaff generator.

Static electricity

Some people guessed that lightning was produced in the same way as the sparks they had seen jumping from person to person. In the 18th century several people died when they flew kites into thunderclouds, trying to capture the sparks of lightning.

We now know that thunderclouds become charged with **static electricity**, created by friction as air particles 'rub' against one another. Eventually the amount of static electricity in the clouds becomes so big that it causes a giant spark which we call lightning.

When you remove your clothes you may sometimes hear crackles and see small sparks. These are caused by static electricity, which builds up on your clothes during the day as they rub against one another and against other materials.

There are two types of static electricity – *positive* electric charge and *negative* electric charge. Some materials are left

Static electricity produces hair-raising effects!

with extra positive charges when they are rubbed with a duster. We say they are positively charged. Other materials are left with extra negative charges when they are rubbed. We say those materials are negatively charged.

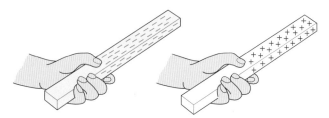

Polythene becomes negatively charged when rubbed with a duster

Perspex becomes positively charged when rubbed with a duster

Both types of static electric charge are produced by friction between the materials that are rubbed together.

Attraction and repulsion

Positive and negative charges exert forces on one another. Charged rods can attract some small objects, such as bits of paper or polystyrene, towards them (like the Greeks' amber). They can even pull (bend) a stream of water.

The forces between electric charges are rather like those between the poles of magnets (remember opposite poles attract one another):

- positive charges attract negative charges,
- negative charges repel (push away) other negative charges,
- positive charges repel (push away) other positive charges.

A negatively charged polythene rod pulls on the positive charges in the water molecules

★ THINGS TO DO

1 a) Put some very small pieces of torn up paper onto the bench. Now rub a polythene rod with a duster for about 10 seconds. That will charge it up with static electricity. Slowly move the rod close to the paper. What do you notice?

b) Try using rods of perspex, wood, glass, copper and any other material you can find. You could also try things like pens, combs and brushes. Polish them up with a duster and see if you get the same effect with the paper.

Make a table showing which materials can be charged and which cannot. Include all of the materials you tested.

2 You will need to make a holder (from paper or plastic) for this experiment. Hang it from a retort stand using cotton.

a) Charge up a polythene rod and rest it in the holder. Charge up another polythene rod. Now bring it (slowly) close to the end of the rod which is in the holder. What happens?

b) Charge up a perspex rod with a piece of polyester material. Put the perspex rod in the holder. Now charge up a polythene rod again. Move it close to the end of the perspex rod. What happens this time?

Make up a table to show what you did and what happened. Try to say why the rods behave the way they do.

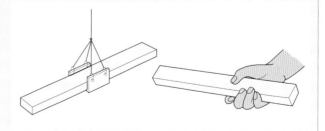

Safety around the home

Electrical faults cause many accidents around the home, including:

- electric shocks to people, some of which are fatal,
- fires, caused when appliances or cables overheat.

Many of these accidents could be avoided by spending a few minutes each week checking cables and plugs. A weekly check could include:

- checking plugs for signs of damage,
- checking cables for signs of wear or other damage,
- untwisting cables, such as those on vacuum cleaners and hairdriers.

WARNING: Never touch electrical items with wet or sweaty hands. Water that contains salts is a conductor (sweat is a salt solution). The current could pass through the moisture, giving you a shock.

Plugs

Plugs are designed to protect you in several ways, as shown below.

The earth connection

You get an electric shock when an electric current passes through your body to the Earth. Most microwave ovens, fridges and

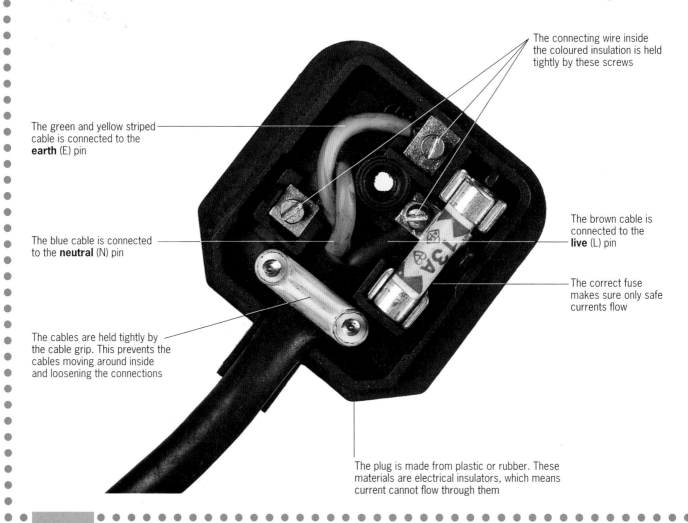

The connecting wire inside the coloured insulation is held tightly by these screws

The green and yellow striped cable is connected to the **earth** (E) pin

The blue cable is connected to the **neutral** (N) pin

The cables are held tightly by the cable grip. This prevents the cables moving around inside and loosening the connections

The brown cable is connected to the **live** (L) pin

The correct fuse makes sure only safe currents flow

The plug is made from plastic or rubber. These materials are electrical insulators, which means current cannot flow through them

If, however, there is a properly connected earth wire, the current goes through it rather than through you. *The earth wire protects you.*

The fuse

If too much current flowed through an appliance it could overheat and cause a fire. To prevent this the current flows through the fuse in the plug. The fuse has a thin strand of wire inside a glass or ceramic tube.

Cartridge fuse

As electricity flows through the fuse, the wire gets hot. If the current is too big the fuse wire melts – the fuse has 'blown'. This makes a gap in the circuit and the current is cut off. A 5 amp (5 A) fuse will melt when the current reaches 5 amps (or thereabouts). A 13 A fuse will melt when the current is bigger than 13 amps. *The fuse protects appliances and helps prevent fire.*

washing machines have metal cases. Metal is a good conductor of electricity. If something went wrong inside these appliances, you could get an electric shock when you touched the case.

★ THINGS TO DO

1 The leaflet shown on the right describes the correct fuses for different appliances. The table below shows which fuses were found in plugs around a house.

Appliance	Fuse fitted	Correct?
Television	3 A	
Washing machine	13 A	
Bedside lamp	13 A	
Hairdrier	3 A	
Kettle	13 A	

Copy the table. Put a tick if the right fuse was fitted. Put a cross if the wrong fuse was used, and write in which fuse should have been used.

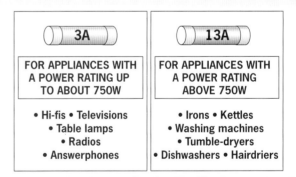

2 Many people do not know how to wire a plug properly. Prepare a leaflet describing:

- how a plug should be properly wired,
- how to choose the correct fuse.

Use lots of diagrams to show people what they must do. Add a checklist at the end of the leaflet so that the readers can make one final check before connecting their plug to the mains supply.

Electricity on the move

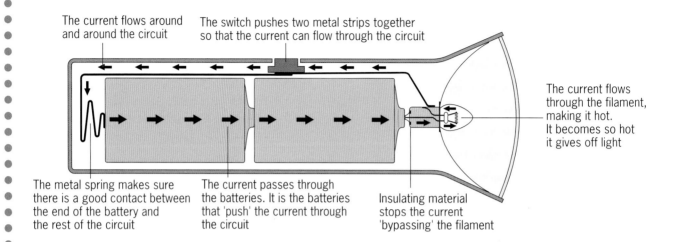

The current flows around and around the circuit

The switch pushes two metal strips together so that the current can flow through the circuit

The current flows through the filament, making it hot. It becomes so hot it gives off light

The metal spring makes sure there is a good contact between the end of the battery and the rest of the circuit

The current passes through the batteries. It is the batteries that 'push' the current through the circuit

Insulating material stops the current 'bypassing' the filament

When a torch is switched on, electric current flows around the circuit, through the bulb and the batteries. The current keeps on going around and around through the bulb.

The current flows only through the metal parts of the torch. The metal parts join together to make up an electric circuit – a loop that goes from the batteries, to the bulb, and then back to the batteries. Electric current will flow only through a complete circuit. If there are any gaps in the circuit (such as when the switch is not pressed) then current cannot flow.

Materials through which an electric current can flow are called **conductors**. Most metals are conductors of electricity. Most non-metals are not conductors – they are called **insulators**. Carbon is an exception – although it is a non-metal it is a conductor of electricity.

Switches

A switch controls the flow of current through a circuit. We can explain this by thinking about the insulators and conductors involved.

When the switch is 'off' there is a gap in the circuit. The gap contains air. Air is an insulator, so current cannot flow through the circuit and the bulb does not light.

When the switch is pressed, the gap closes. The two metal parts in the switch are conductors of electricity. There is now a complete circuit (or loop) so current flows through the circuit and the bulb lights.

Electric current can flow only through complete conducting circuits.

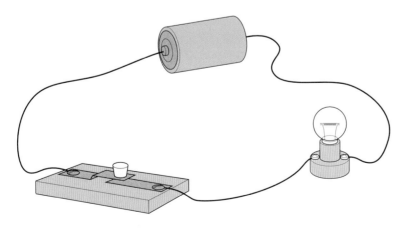

A simple on/off switch

Most switches in your home use the same idea. The one shown here is found on a battery-powered car vacuum cleaner.

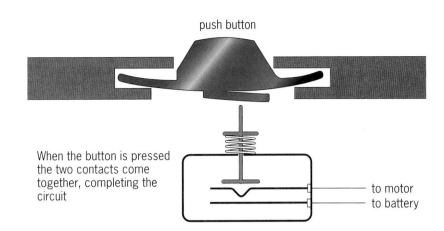

push button

When the button is pressed the two contacts come together, completing the circuit

to motor
to battery

★ THINGS TO DO

1 a) Take a switch from a doorbell apart. Look carefully at the parts inside the switch. Draw what you see and write a sentence describing how you think the switch works.

b) Connect the switch to the bell. Does the bell work when you press the switch? If not, find out what you have done wrong.

2 Cut the plastic off a short length of electrical connecting wire. Keep the metal wire from the centre.

Use the circuit on the right to test the plastic. Then test the metal wire.

a) Copy and complete these sentences:

The _____ is a conductor.

The _____ is an insulator.

b) Someone said 'the plastic is there to protect you'. How does it protect you?

c) How could a damaged cable, such as the one shown in the photo, be dangerous?

3 Design and build a small electric fan which could be used to cool you down in the summer. Your design should include a switch and a case for the batteries. Think about the equipment you will need and how you will connect your circuit.

Draw your design, build it and then test it to make sure it works.

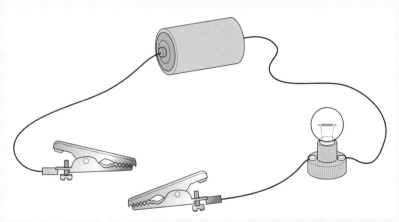

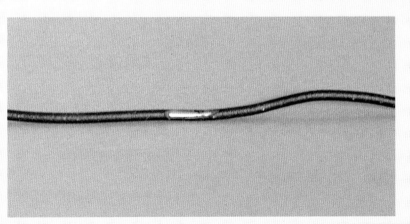

2.4 Drawing electric circuits

So far we have drawn circuits using pictures of the parts. Proper circuit diagrams are drawn using symbols instead of pictures. Some common symbols are shown alongside.

When there are 2 or 3 parts, such as bulbs, then 2 or 3 symbols are joined together. Two bulbs, for example, would be shown as:

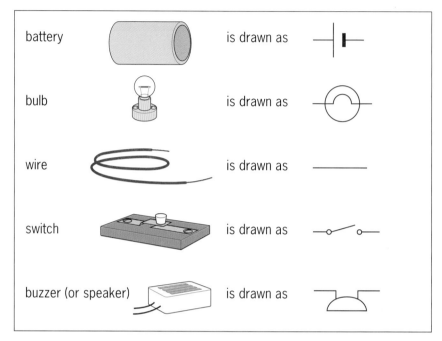

battery		is drawn as	
bulb		is drawn as	
wire		is drawn as	
switch		is drawn as	
buzzer (or speaker)		is drawn as	

The use of symbols makes it much easier to draw circuits. This circuit, for example,

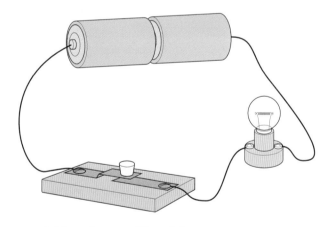

would be drawn like this:

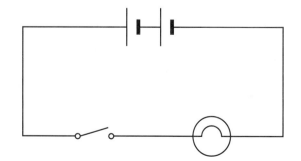

Notice that:
- the wires are drawn as straight lines, formed into a rectangular 'loop';
- each component is in the same place in both diagrams.

Series and parallel circuits

The circuit shown here has a single loop. The current from the batteries flows through the switch (when it is pressed), then through the bulb and buzzer, before returning to the batteries. These 'single loop' circuits have the parts connected in **series**.

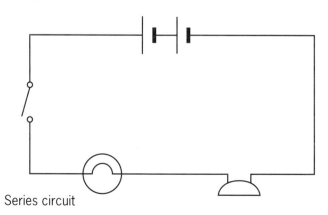

Series circuit

Series circuits are not often used because either everything must be switched ON or everything must be switched OFF. One part cannot work if the others are off. If your house lights were connected like this, when you wanted to switch on your living room light every other light would need to be switched on. The problem can be solved by connecting the parts in a different way – in **parallel**. This means joining them in several loops. Each loop has its own switch.

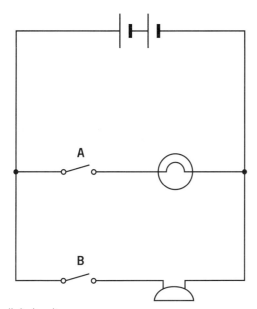

Parallel circuit

You can see that if switch A is pressed, the lamp will light. The buzzer will not sound. If, on the other hand, switch B is pressed, the buzzer will sound but the lamp will not light.

The parts in a parallel circuit can be switched on and off separately. One part can be on even if everything else is off.

★ **THINGS TO DO**

1 Write out a list of the parts needed to build each of the circuits shown below.

a) A buzzer circuit for your bedroom door

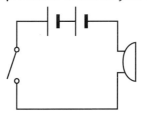

b) A control circuit for a model car

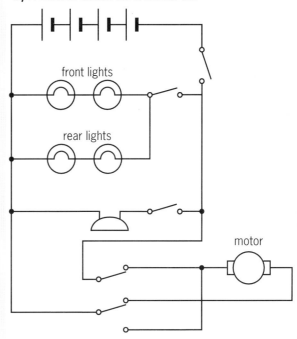

2 John's computer was just behind the door of his bedroom. His sister kept taking it without telling him. He decided to fit an alarm on the door to his bedroom. He thought he would use a bulb to show when someone opened the door, and a buzzer to show if someone lifted the computer off the desk.

Design an alarm system that would do the job for him. You will have to design and test the switches. Make a model door.

When you are sure the circuit works, draw it, adding any notes that you think would help others to build the circuit. (You could pass your design to other people and see if they can build it using your instructions.)

Power suppliers

Every electrical device which you use needs just the right amount of power to make it work properly. The power can be supplied by batteries, or from the 'mains' supply to your home. The higher the **voltage** of the supply, the more power it can deliver to a circuit. Voltage is measured in **volts** (V).

If a device does not get just the right amount of power then it will not work properly. The car battery below, for example, could not supply the power needed by the hairdrier.

This personal stereo needs two 1.5 volt (1.5 V) batteries to supply the power for the motor to work

Work and power

In all circuits the power supply pushes current through the circuit to operate the device. We can say that the power supply does **work** (pushing current around the circuit) to operate the device. For example, the battery in the circuit below does work to light the lamp.

A 12 volt battery is needed to supply the power for the circuits in cars

The 230 volt mains supply is needed for most of the devices in your home

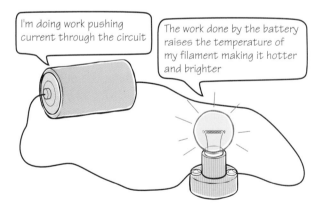

I'm doing work pushing current through the circuit

The work done by the battery raises the temperature of my filament making it hotter and brighter

This is the **power** of the bulb (40 **watts**). It is the amount of work that must be done every second by the supply to light the bulb

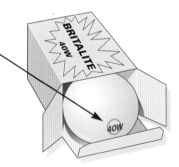

A battery cannot do enough work to light the bulbs in our homes. They need a much more powerful supply. The voltage of our mains supply is 230 volts.

When we buy bulbs for the home we might choose a 40 watt (40 W) or a 100 watt (100 W) bulb.

A 100 watt bulb needs more **power** to get it to work properly. The mains supply pushes a bigger current through the bulb. Energy is transferred faster and the bulb is therefore brighter than a 40 watt bulb.

Power can be measured in **watts** or **kilowatts**. 1 kilowatt is equal to 1000 watts.

Current

The size of the current flowing through a circuit is measured in **amperes**, normally shortened to **amps** (or A). Some things work with quite small currents. Others need much bigger currents to work properly.

An ammeter is used to measure the electric current flowing through a circuit. The ammeter is connected in line with everything else in the circuit – it is connected *in series* with the rest of the circuit.

This is the usual symbol for an ammeter.

A calculator needs a current of about $\frac{1}{50}$th of an amp. Too much current would damage the parts of the circuit

A kettle needs a current of about 5 amps. If too little current flowed the kettle would either not work, or it would take ages to boil the water

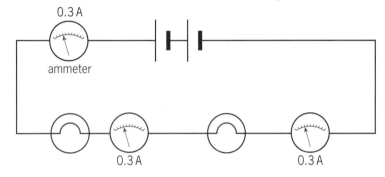

In a series circuit the current is the same at all points

★ THINGS TO DO

1 A diagram like this is found in the battery compartment of some personal CD players.
a) How many batteries are needed?

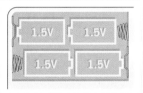

Helen connected the batteries like this.
b) Why did the CD player not work?
c) What should she do? Draw how she should connect them.

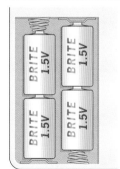

2 A pupil built a small car using Lego. She added an electric motor with a battery and measured how far the car moved in 3 seconds. She then did the same using 2 batteries, then 3, then 4. The table shows her results.

Number of batteries	How far the car moved in 3 seconds
1	50 cm
2	70 cm
3	100 cm
4	120 cm

a) Draw the axes for a graph. The vertical axis (the one that goes up) should be for distance moved. The horizontal axis (the one that goes across) should show the number of batteries.
b) Now mark points on the graph for each pair of values in the table.
c) Write a sentence saying what pattern you can see in the graph.
d) What do you think would happen if she used 5 batteries?

Electric current

In a simple circuit such as the one shown here the battery pushes current through the circuit. The **electric current** is a flow of tiny charged particles called electrons through the wires.

If 2 bulbs are used the battery finds it more difficult to push the current through the circuit. The current decreases and the bulbs are dimmer.

Each bulb (and everything else that we might put into a circuit) puts up some **resistance** against the flow of current. Connecting wire, bulbs, motors, buzzers, bells – even the battery – resist the flow of current.

The more devices there are in a series circuit, the bigger the resistance and the smaller the current.

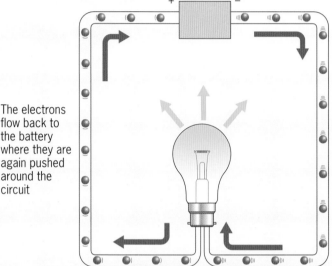

A chemical reaction inside the battery pushes the electrons in the metal wires so they flow through the circuit

The electrons flow back to the battery where they are again pushed around the circuit

The electrons all move in the same direction through the wires to the bulb

The electrons heat up the filament of the bulb as they flow through it. The filament gets very hot and gives out light

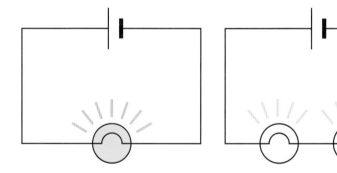

Two bulbs resist the flow of current more than one, so the current is smaller and the bulbs are dimmer

Well in control

Lots of things around your home work the way they do because you are able to control the current that flows through them. For example:

- dimmer switches adjust the brightness of your room lights;
- the control on an iron adjusts its temperature;
- volume controls adjust the loudness of your television or hi-fi;
- fast forward and rewind controls on your video recorder make the tape wind faster.

These control devices all work because they change the resistance in the circuit. Changing the resistance changes the current.

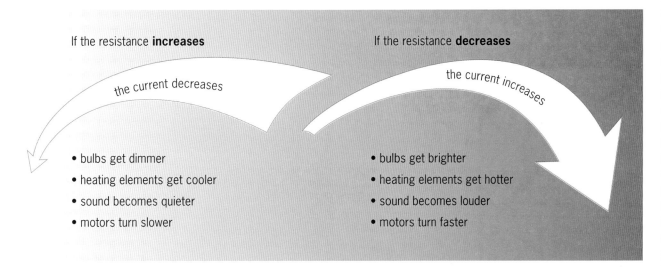

If the resistance **increases**

the current decreases

- bulbs get dimmer
- heating elements get cooler
- sound becomes quieter
- motors turn slower

If the resistance **decreases**

the current increases

- bulbs get brighter
- heating elements get hotter
- sound becomes louder
- motors turn faster

The wire that we normally use to connect circuits has a very low resistance. It has very little effect on the current. Other metals have a higher resistance. Wire made using these metals is called resistance wire. By changing the amount of resistance wire in the circuit, we can increase or decrease the current.

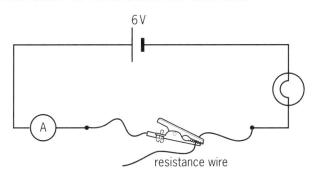

The amount of resistance wire in the circuit can be changed by sliding the clip along the wire

The volume controls on your radio, television or hi-fi use a variable resistance to change the current flowing to the speakers. The bigger the current, the louder the sound.

★ THINGS TO DO

1 Build the dimmer circuit shown above. Test the circuit by sliding the clip along the resistance wire. Copy and complete these sentences:

As the wire gets longer, the brightness of the bulb gets _____ and the current _____ .

As the wire gets shorter, the brightness of the bulb gets _____ and the current _____ .

2 Try replacing the bulb in your last circuit with a buzzer. What happens when you change the length of resistance wire now?

3 Try a motor in place of the bulb. Make a note about what happens when the current changes.

Fatal attraction

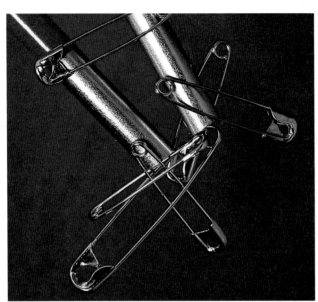

Magnetic attraction

Magnets attract iron and steel (and a few other metal alloys). Most of you will, at some time, have picked up paper clips or pins using a magnet. They are pulled towards the magnet (attracted to it) because they contain iron. If the magnet is strong enough it can make the objects move even though they might be several centimetres away – magnets can pull from a distance. Imagine what fun that could have been in the Middle Ages when knights wore suits of armour!

The space around a magnet in which this attraction occurs is called the **magnetic field**. Things will only be affected if they are in the magnetic field. The stronger the magnet, the further the magnetic field extends.

Different types of magnet

Magnets may have different shapes and be made from different materials. Many good quality magnets are made from alloys that are mixtures of metals such as steel, cobalt and nickel.

All magnets have one thing in common – one end (or side) will be the North pole and the opposite end (or side) will be a South pole. If a bar magnet was free to move, the North pole would always swing around and end up pointing towards the North Pole of the Earth. (The name 'North' pole comes from the original description of 'North-seeking' pole.)

Magnets come in different shapes and sizes

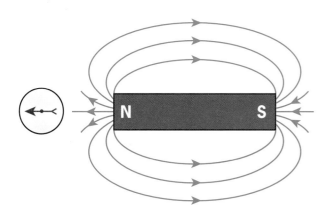

A magnetic field is drawn as arrowed lines from North pole to South pole. They show the direction in which a plotting compass would point if it were placed there

If two magnets are brought close to one another with their North poles facing, they push away from one another, or repel. The same happens if two South poles are brought close together. If, however, a North pole is brought close to a South pole they will pull together, or attract. The rule is:

similar poles repel, opposite poles attract

The plastic seal around this door contains magnets. It is pulled towards the main compartment of the fridge, holding the door closed

What are magnets used for?

It might seem as if you rarely see magnets at work. They are around, in lots of places that might be missed:

- inside loudspeakers, where they make the speaker cone move to-and-fro;
- as part of every motor, including those in the vacuum cleaner, electric drill, washing machine, CD and tape player, and video cassette recorder;
- on cupboard doors, especially those in kitchen units – the magnets hold the doors closed;
- in fridge and freezer door seals.

★ THINGS TO DO

1 Some reed relays contain two thin pieces of steel which just touch one another. If a magnet is brought close to them they pull apart.

Design a circuit using a reed relay, a magnet, a buzzer (or bell) and batteries that could be used as a door alarm. The alarm should sound if the door is opened.

You could make a model door (using card) to test your design. When it is working tell others in your class how it works.

2 The metal in a reed relay is steel. Do some tests to find out what other materials could be used. Make a table showing materials which are magnetic (attracted by magnets) and those which are non-magnetic.

3 Plan and carry out tests to find out which of the magnets in your classroom/laboratory is strongest.

Magnetic effects

The photograph shows scrap metal being lifted by a large magnet. This magnet can be switched on and off. It is an **electromagnet**.

The magnet is a large circular piece of 'soft' iron. Thousands of turns of wire are wrapped around it. When an electric current flows through the wire the soft iron becomes magnetised. It then attracts the scrap iron and steel. When the current is switched off, the soft iron loses its magnetism and the scrap metal falls. ('Soft' means that the iron loses its magnetism when the current is switched off.)

This scrapyard hoist works by electromagnetism

What causes electromagnetism?

When an electric current flows through a wire it creates a magnetic field around the wire. The magnetic field is very weak – far too small to attract things. The magnetic field becomes stronger if the wire is formed into a coil, called a solenoid. The coil then behaves in a similar way to a bar magnet. One end acts as a North pole and the other as a South pole.

If the direction of the current is reversed then the North pole becomes a South pole (and the South pole becomes a North pole). Reversing the direction of the current reverses the poles.

The magnetic field becomes much stronger if the wire is wrapped around a soft iron bar. When current flows through the coil, the iron itself becomes magnetised. The bar acts like a permanent magnet, with a North and a South pole. But if the current stops flowing, the bar loses its magnetism almost immediately.

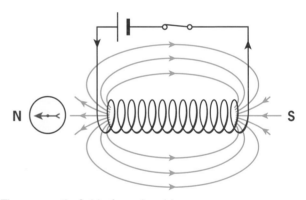

The magnetic field of a solenoid

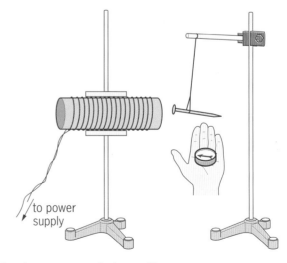

An electromagnet behaves like a permanent magnet when the current is flowing

The electromagnet can be made stronger by:

- increasing the number of coils of wire,
- increasing the current.

Who is at the door?

When the push-button switch on a doorbell is pressed a current flows through the coils of a small electromagnet inside the bell unit. It becomes magnetised and attracts a soft iron plate, causing the 'striker' to strike the bell. But the circuit is then immediately broken at the 'make-and-break' contact so the electromagnet loses its magnetism. The spring pulls the soft iron plate back, remaking the circuit at the make-and-break

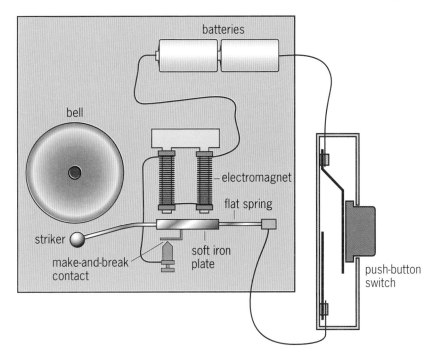

An electromagnet makes your doorbell ring

contact and the striker strikes again. This is repeated as long as the push button is pressed, so the bell keeps chiming.

★ THINGS TO DO

1 Copper (1p and 2p) coins issued after 1992 are made from steel, plated with copper. Before 1992 they contained no steel. Check this yourself using a magnet.

2 Imagine that the Royal Mint (the people who make our coins) want to take all the old copper coins (made before 1992) out of use. A pupil designed this machine to help them.

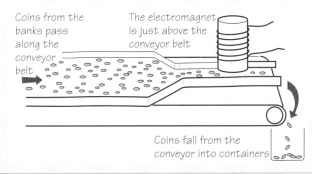

Coins from the banks pass along the conveyor belt

The electromagnet is just above the conveyor belt

Coins fall from the conveyor into containers

a) How do you think this machine will work? Will it separate the coins?

b) Which coins will fall into the container at the end of the conveyor?

c) What will happen to the other coins?

3 Build the electromagnet shown in the picture alongside. Set the power supply to 4 V d.c. and test your electromagnet. How many 2p coins can it hold? How many 1p coins can it hold?

Plan and carry out a test to find out if the number of coins that the electromagnet can hold depends on the number of coils of wire used.

Write a report saying how your results could affect the model recommended to the Royal Mint to separate coins.

Human dynamo

Some bicycles have a **dynamo** which supplies the power for the lights. You do work when you pedal the bicycle. Some of the work you do turns the dynamo. The dynamo produces a small voltage which drives current through the circuit, lighting the lights.

The faster the dynamo rotates, the bigger the current and the brighter the light.

Inside a bicycle dynamo is a strong permanent magnet. The magnet is turned quickly by the wheel. The magnet is surrounded by a large coil of wire wound on soft iron. A voltage is produced in the coil as the magnetic field rotates through the wires forming the coil. The voltage drives current through the circuit.

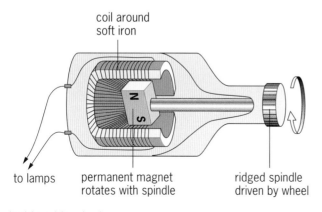

coil around
soft iron

to lamps   permanent magnet
rotates with spindle

ridged spindle
driven by wheel

Inside a bicycle dynamo

Stop thief!

Many clothing shops now have anti-theft systems fitted around the doors. Everything in the shop is fitted with a magnet. The magnet is taken off the clothes when you pay.

Around the doorway there is a large coil of wire. If someone tries to leave without paying, the magnet on the clothes creates a small current in the coil which sets off the alarm. The electric current is produced when the magnetic field of the magnet moves through the coil of wire.

Size of the current

A galvanometer can detect very small electric currents. The ends of a coil of wire can be connected to a galvanometer. If a magnet is now moved into, or out of, the coil, a small current is detected by the galvanometer.

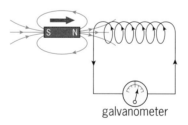

When the magnet is moving into the coil a current flows

galvanometer

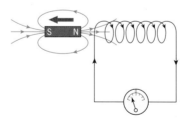

When the magnet is moving out of the coil a current flows in the opposite direction

The size of the current can be increased by:

- moving the magnet faster,
- using stronger magnets which have a stronger magnetic field,
- making more loops of wire on the coil.

★ THINGS TO DO

1 Follow these instructions to build your own shop alarm system.

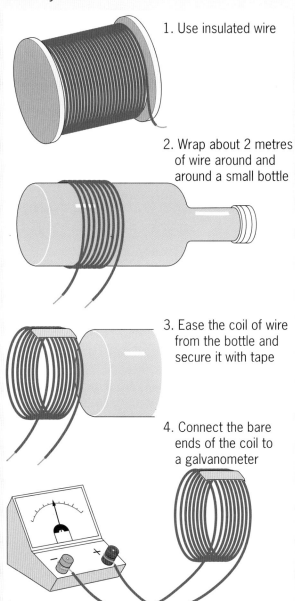

1. Use insulated wire

2. Wrap about 2 metres of wire around and around a small bottle

3. Ease the coil of wire from the bottle and secure it with tape

4. Connect the bare ends of the coil to a galvanometer

Try putting a small magnet into a handkerchief and passing it through the coil. Does the meter show some current? When you are sure it works well, show someone how it works.

Try to change the system so that it produces a bigger current when the magnet passes through.

Write a letter to a manufacturing company explaining your design and how it works. Say how it could be made really sensitive, and how it would be used in a shop.

2 A pupil made this model wind generator using a bicycle dynamo.

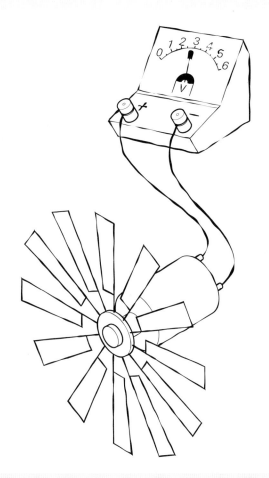

The wind blew the blades which turned the dynamo. The electric current from the dynamo made a bulb light. Sometimes it was very dim. At other times it was very bright. He thought there must be more voltage at some times than others. His brother measured the voltage at different wind speeds. This is what he wrote down:

When the wind was very strong the voltage was 7 volts; as the wind dropped, the voltage was 4 volts. When the wind was just sufficient to turn the blades it was 1 volt.

a) Put the results into a table. Draw a bar chart using your table.
b) Does the information in the table tell you whether there is a connection between the wind speed and voltage? What is the connection?

Electricity to your home

All change!

The current that flows through battery-powered circuits is called **direct current** (**d.c.**) because it flows in one direction all of the time. The current from the sockets in your home is **alternating current** (**a.c.**). Alternating current 'pulses' to and fro, changing direction 50 times every second. This is mains electricity.

Mains electricity is made in power stations (or generating stations). In a coal-fired power station the heat produced by burning coal is used to heat water in a boiler. The steam (produced at very high pressure) is used to drive turbines connected to a generator.

The electricity that you use today could come from any of the power stations connected to the National Grid – not necessarily the one nearest your home.

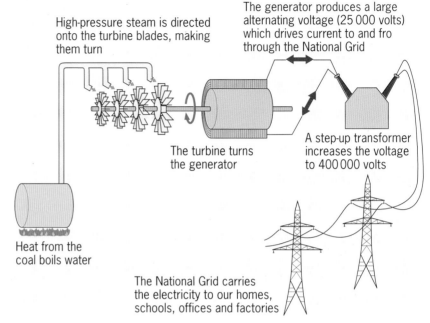

High-pressure steam is directed onto the turbine blades, making them turn

The generator produces a large alternating voltage (25 000 volts) which drives current to and fro through the National Grid

The turbine turns the generator

A step-up transformer increases the voltage to 400 000 volts

Heat from the coal boils water

The National Grid carries the electricity to our homes, schools, offices and factories

The generation of mains electricity

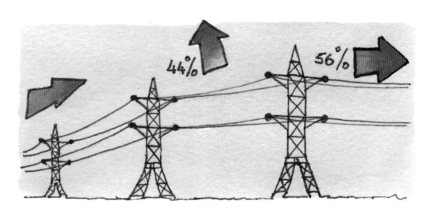

44% of the energy that enters the National Grid would be lost if the voltage was 25 000 volts

Hot wires

When electricity flows through any cable or wire, it makes the wire hot. Electricity flowing through the Grid is no exception – those cables also get hot. The heat is wasted energy.

To reduce the amount of energy lost, the voltage output from power stations is increased from 25 000 volts a.c. to 400 000 volts a.c. Increasing the voltage decreases the current. A smaller current means less energy is wasted as heat. The voltage is changed by a **transformer**. A 'step-up' transformer increases the voltage. The energy losses are reduced to only 1% when transformers are used in this way.

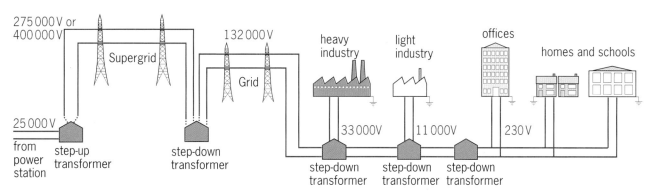

Throughout the National Grid, transformers increase and decrease the voltage at various points

Eventually, before the electricity enters your home, a 'step-down' transformer reduces the voltage to 230 volts a.c. – the 'mains voltage'. All mains electrical appliances sold in this country are built to work at this voltage. They will not work at any voltage outside the range 220–250 volts.

★ THINGS TO DO

1 This graph shows how much electricity is needed (throughout the whole country) at different times during the day.

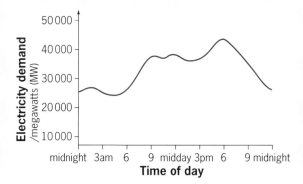

a) When is most electricity needed?
b) Why do you think most electricity is needed then?
c) When is least electricity needed?
d) Why is so little electricity needed then?
e) Sometimes, when there is something special like the FA Cup Final on television, extra electricity is needed. The electricity generating companies must plan ahead so that they can provide the extra. Write down two other occurrences that might mean extra electricity would be needed.
f) The graph is for a day in winter. Draw another graph showing what you think it might look like in summer.

2 Sometimes the electricity generating companies need to increase or decrease the voltage of the supply. What do they use to do that?

3 These charts show how much of our electricity was produced in different ways in 1990 and 1995.

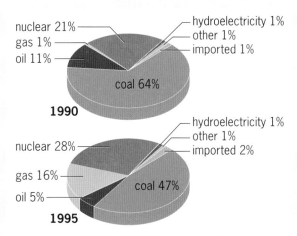

a) Which method provided most of our electricity in 1995?
b) What do you think 'other' sources might be?
c) Why do you think the use of oil fell by 6% between 1990 and 1995?
d) How much less electricity (as a percentage) was produced from coal in 1995 compared with 1990? Can you suggest why?
e) Why do you think we import electricity (buy it from other countries)?

Drawing bar charts

You can put your results into a bar chart when the thing you changed in your investigation is described in words (see page 20). The results below, for example, can be put into a bar chart because the type of ball can only be described in words – you either use one ball or another. Notice that the results have already been arranged in order.

Type of golf ball	How high it bounced when we dropped it from 100 cm above the ground/cm
Polnud	71
Topol	76
Trueflight	82
Sprint	87

The descriptions used in this column (the type of ball) always go along the horizontal (bottom) axis

The thing that was measured (the height of bounce) always goes on the vertical (up) axis

Notice that the values on the axis go from 0 to 100 and are equally spaced. You do not use only the values that were measured

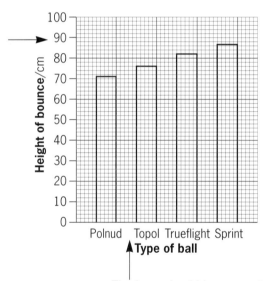

Now you can see how each ball compares with the others.

The bars should be separated on a chart like this

★ THINGS TO DO

Draw bar charts for the results shown here.

1

Type of acid	How long it took to dissolve 5 cm magnesium ribbon/s
hydrochloric	21
sulphuric	28
nitric	34

2

Where we grew the plant	How much it grew in 14 days/cm
in the dark	0
dim light	2
normal room	3
bright light	5

3

FORCES

Forces and their effects

'Granny's car won't start. Give her a push!'

If you push hard enough the car will begin to move. The 'push' exerts a **force** on the car, which makes the car begin to move. Without that force the car would stay still. You could also pull the car with a rope. That force would have the same effect – it would make the car begin to move.

A force is needed to start things moving.

To get it moving faster an 'extra' force is needed. With a little help from your friends you can get the car to speed up – providing they push in the right direction.

The 'extra' force makes the car speed up.
Now you didn't realise that Granny is a daredevil bungee jumper. Once she jumps that's it – she'll keep on falling . . .

and falling . . . and falling. The force of gravity (a force that pulls things towards the Earth) makes her speed up . . .

. . . until the cord tightens. It will then exert a force in the opposite direction to her movement, which will slow her down. Eventually it will stop her falling.

A force is needed to slow things down, or to stop them moving.

And now you're at the fair. You're heading straight across the bumper track when suddenly Granny hits you from the side. Ouch!

Here the force of the other car changes your direction.

So what are forces?

In each of the examples on the opposite page you can see that forces affect the way things move. Forces can:

- make things begin to move,
- make things speed up,
- make things slow down,
- make things change direction.

When you see any of these things happening around you then forces are at work.

The forces can be large or small. Sometimes a small force will make something start to move. At other times a larger force is needed.

A much smaller force is needed to make the pram move than is needed to move the car

Measuring forces

In the laboratory forces are measured using a forcemeter. The size of the force can be seen on the scale. The units for force are **newtons** (written as N).

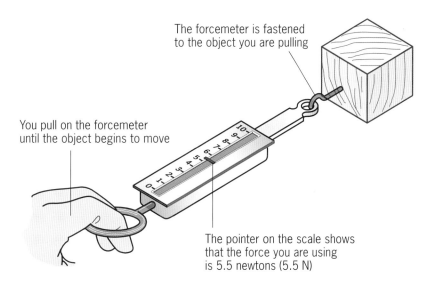

The forcemeter is fastened to the object you are pulling

You pull on the forcemeter until the object begins to move

The pointer on the scale shows that the force you are using is 5.5 newtons (5.5 N)

★ THINGS TO DO

1 Measure the force needed to do each of these things. Make a note of the force needed to do each job.
   a) Lift a textbook from the bench.
   b) Pull a piece of sticky tape from the bench.
   c) Pull down the handle on the classroom door.
   d) Stretch an elastic band by 5 cm.
   e) Pull a piece of paper from a lump of Blu-tack.
   f) Open a clothes peg.
   g) Pull two pieces of Velcro apart.
   h) Crush a grape.

2 Get 3 or 4 different brands of sticky tape. Use your forcemeter to find out which is the stickiest. Write your results in a table.
   Design an advert for the strongest brand of tape. Use your results in the advert to convince people that this brand is best. Include a bar chart showing your results.

Balancing forces

When someone stands on your toes you scream in pain. That is because their weight pushes on your toes. Weight is a force – the force due to **gravity**. If you hold something in the air then let go, its weight makes it fall to the ground.

In weight-lifting competitions the bar and weights must be held steady for several seconds.

The weights will be pushing *down* on the weightlifter's arms. If their weight was the only force at work here, then the weights would crash back to Earth. They don't fall because the weightlifter is pushing *up* on them. The upward force must balance the downward force if the weights are to be held steady.

On diagrams, the forces are shown as arrows. The direction and length of the arrow give you an indication of the direction and size of the force – the longer the arrow, the bigger the force.

There are balanced forces (forces that are the same size but act in opposite directions) acting on things that are not moving.

If extra weight is added to the bar, the downward force will increase. To keep the weights steady, the weightlifter would have to increase the 'pushing up' force so that it balanced the weight. Eventually, however, he will reach the stage where he cannot push hard enough. The downward force (due to the weight) will be bigger than the upward force (exerted by the lifter). The weights will then fall to the ground.

Since one force is bigger than the other, the 'extra' force makes the weights begin to move. They move in the direction of the 'extra' force.

The weightlifter must push up

The forces are equal in size and act in opposite directions

The downward force is bigger than the upward force

Reaction forces

When you stand on the ground you exert a force on the ground because of your weight. You are not moving, so there must be an equal and opposite force which balances your weight. The force that pushes up on you is a **reaction force** exerted by the ground.

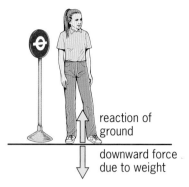

reaction of ground

downward force due to weight

The ground exerts an equal and opposite reaction force so you do not sink

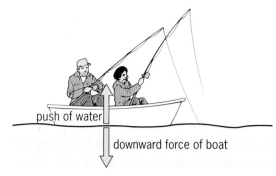

push of water

downward force of boat

The boat exerts a downward force on the water. The water exerts an equal and opposite reaction force which balances the downward force so the boat floats

★ THINGS TO DO

1 a) Stretch a rubber band by 2 or 3 cm as shown in the picture.

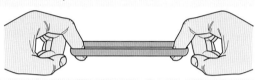

Can you feel the band pulling back on your fingers? What happens if you pull harder? What do you feel now?

Write a sentence saying what happened.

b) Try the same with a spring. Again, write a sentence saying what happened.

c) Now try squashing a spring. Again, write about any forces that you feel.

2 a) When an empty bottle is put into water a force holds it up – the force stops it sinking. Try pushing a plastic bottle into water. What do you feel? Try pushing it further into water. What difference do you notice? What do you think is making the force?

b) Use half a bottle to imitate a boat. Float it on water. Draw a mark on the side of the boat showing the water level.

Now put a 5 N weight in the boat. Make a new mark showing where the water level is now.

Add more weights, 5 N at a time, and make a new mark each time.

Write a sentence saying what happens to the boat as more and more weight is added.

Can you explain what you have seen?

c) When you hire pleasure boats there is often a sign saying how many people are allowed in the boat. Why do you think the sign is important?

d) Some pupils made this table using the results of their experiment.

Weight in the boat	Depth of boat below water level
0 N	1 cm
5 N	5 cm
10 N	9 cm
15 N	12 cm
20 N	15 cm
25 N	17 cm

i) Draw a graph using their results. Put *Weight in the boat* on the axis across, and *How deep it was under the water* on the axis up.
ii) How much weight was needed to make the boat sink 8 cm below water level?
iii) If the boat went 14 cm under water, how much weight would be in it?
iv) Their model boat had a depth of 21 cm. How much weight would be needed to make the top of the boat reach water level?

At a stretch

Imagine what happens when you pull on a rubber band. If you pull the band at one end, only one force acts. The band begins to move in the direction in which you pull it.

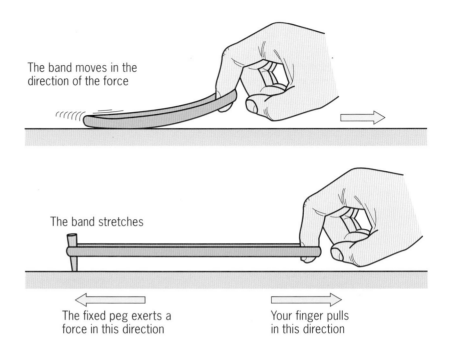

The band moves in the direction of the force

If, however, you fasten one end of the band and pull on the other, the band stretches. The rubber is deformed (its shape is changed) because there are two forces at work, acting in opposite directions. The two outward forces place the rubber band under **tension**.

The band stretches

The fixed peg exerts a force in this direction

Your finger pulls in this direction

Restoring forces

When you stretch a rubber band in this way you feel the rubber pulling back on your fingers. This is due to a **restoring force** exerted by the stretched rubber. If the band is stretched, then held steady, there are in fact two forces at work on each end – a pulling outward force and the pulling inward force of the band. The band is not moving so the forces on each end must be balanced.

To stretch the band further, you must exert a bigger force on it (you must pull harder). The restoring force would increase, so the inward-acting forces on the peg and your finger would also increase.

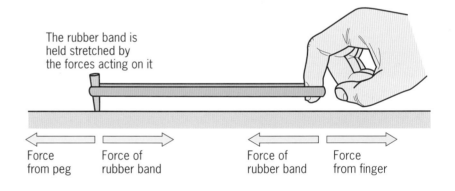

The rubber band is held stretched by the forces acting on it

Force from peg | Force of rubber band | Force of rubber band | Force from finger

Bungee jumping

A bungee cord must be fastened at the top if it is to stop the person who is jumping. The jumper is slowed down by the upward (restoring) force created as the rubber bungee cord stretches.

If the bungee cord did not stretch it would stop the jumper too suddenly. The sudden jerk would cause serious injuries.

At first the cord runs slack above the jumpers. The only force acting is the weight of the jumpers, which makes them speed up towards the ground

Then the cord begins to stretch as the jumpers pull on it. The stretched rubber creates an upward (restoring) force which begins to slow them down

Eventually the jumpers will be stopped by the cord. The upward force will be bigger than the downward force so they will begin to move upwards again!

Not just rubber

Other materials also stretch when forces are at work on them.

In all cases the materials are deformed by the effects of at least two forces acting on them in different directions.

Bubble gum is stretched by the push of the air inside it

This watch strap can be stretched to pass it over your hand

★ THINGS TO DO

1 You know that rubber and springs are stretched when forces act on them.

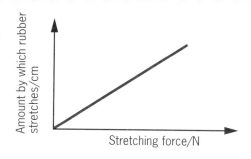

Do wires stretch in the same way?
a) Plan how you could find out whether copper wire stretches in a similar way when weights are hung from it. Think about how you can make sure you (and others) will be safe.
b) Carry out your test when your teacher is satisfied with your plan.

c) Put your results into a table. Use them to draw a graph or chart.
d) Say what you found out from your investigation. What happens to the length of the wire as more and more weight is added?

2 Alan needs a balance to weigh the fish he catches. His Mum said 'You can make a balance with a spring.'
a) Plan and carry out a test to find out how the length of a spring changes when more and more weight is added.
b) Draw a graph or chart using your results.
c) Say what you found out about the connection between the length of a spring and the weight on it.
d) How could you use the spring to make a balance for weighing fish? Your teacher may let you try making one.

Squashed

The landing mats used in high jumping (or pole vaulting) contain foam rubber (rubber with lots of air bubbles in it). When the high jumper lands on the mat the rubber is squashed between her and the ground.

The jumper exerts a downward force on the mat. The ground exerts a force which pushes up on the mat.

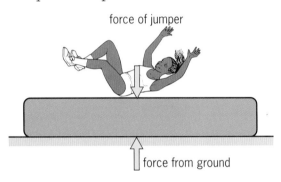

force of jumper

force from ground

It is these two forces, acting in opposite directions, which squash – or compress – the foam rubber. It is said to be in a state of **compression**. As it is compressed the rubber exerts a restoring force, and it pushes back on the jumper, slowing her down.

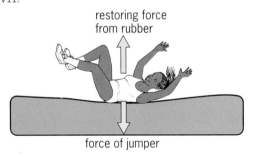

restoring force from rubber

force of jumper

This helps prevent injuries which could occur if she landed on hard ground, which would stop her suddenly with a much bigger force.

The air inside bouncy castles does a similar job. When you land on a bouncy castle, the air becomes squashed, 'soaking up' the bump.

A safe landing

Springs, like foam, are squashed by forces that push inwards on them.

The bigger the force, the more the spring is squashed

The mattress on your bed may contain many springs, each joined together. Some are squashed more than others when you lie down, so the mattress takes up the same shape as your body. That makes it more comfortable. When you get out of bed the springs 'spring back' and the mattress returns to its original shape.

Not so easily squashed

Liquids are not so easily compressed as air, because the particles in a liquid are close together. This makes liquids useful in **hydraulic systems**, such as those that operate the brakes on a car. The picture shows how the brake oil 'passes' the force from the pedals to the brakes.

The system works only because the oil cannot be easily compressed. If air (at normal pressure) was used, it would simply squash up inside the pipes. If the brakes worked at all, they would work too slowly. With liquid they react much more quickly to any movement of the brake pedal.

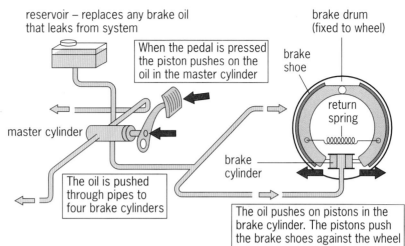

reservoir – replaces any brake oil that leaks from system

When the pedal is pressed the piston pushes on the oil in the master cylinder

master cylinder

The oil is pushed through pipes to four brake cylinders

brake drum (fixed to wheel)

brake shoe

return spring

brake cylinder

The oil pushes on pistons in the brake cylinder. The pistons push the brake shoes against the wheel

Hydraulic brakes

★ THINGS TO DO

1 Some elderly people have difficulty squeezing plastic bottles, such as those used for washing-up liquid. Test 3 or 4 different types of 'squeezy bottle' to find out whether one kind of bottle is easier to squash than others.
  Write a report of your tests.

2 Divers use bottles containing compressed air. They breathe the air when they are under water. Compressed air is simply air that has been squashed so you can get lots of it into a small space.
  This picture shows the air particles inside a full bottle. (There would be millions of them, the picture shows only a few.)

a) Draw the bottle and show the air particles in it after half the air has been used.
b) Draw the bottle again, showing the air particles in it just before the air runs out.

3 The picture below shows a hydraulic jack that can be used to lift a car. A liquid is used to pass the force from the handle to the car.

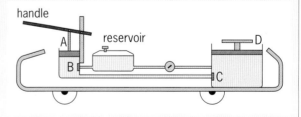

handle

reservoir

A

B

D

C

a) When the handle is pushed down, what happens to the piston marked A?
b) What does piston A do to the liquid in the pipes?
c) Why does valve C move when the handle is pushed down?
d) What causes piston D to lift the car?

3.5 Well bent

The plank in the picture bends when someone moves to the end. To understand why it bends, we need to think about the forces that are at work on each end of the plank.

The person pushes down on this end of the plank. The other end of the plank is fastened (it cannot move) so the plank bends. As it bends the wood exerts a restoring force and pushes upwards on the person on the plank

This end of the plank is fastened to the boat. If someone is standing on the opposite end, this part of the plank will be pulled upwards. To prevent this end moving, the downward force (from the boat) must balance this upward force

Some materials spring back into their original shape after being deformed (squashed, bent or stretched). This sort of behaviour is described as **elastic**. This does not mean the material is made from elastic – the word elastic describes how the material behaves.

Other materials do not spring back into shape. They stay deformed. This sort of behaviour is described as **plastic**. Once again, this does not mean the material is made from plastic – the word is used to describe what happens to the material when a deforming force acts on it.

Steel (like most materials) shows elastic behaviour when small forces act on it. A car bonnet, for example, will spring back into shape if it is pressed lightly. Bigger forces, however, bend the steel permanently. It then behaves as a plastic material.

This bottle springs back into shape when you stop squashing it

Plasticine keeps its new shape after being deformed

Large forces can cause permanent damage

The size of a force affects how much a material is deformed.

A diving board is designed to bend. As it bends it exerts an upward force on the diver which balances the downward force of his or her weight. To make it stronger (so that it would not bend as much) we could:

A light person bends the board by only a small amount

A heavier person bends the board more because of the bigger downward force

- use a different material,
- use the same material but make it thicker, or
- use the same material but make it shorter.

★ THINGS TO DO

1 Mr Jones was building bookshelves. When he put the books on this shelf it bent too much.

He said 'I think it won't bend quite so much if I put the brackets closer together'. His wife said 'I think you need thicker wood'.

Talk about their ideas with your friends. What do you think affects how much the shelf will bend? Make a note of your ideas.

Test each idea using the method shown below. Don't forget to make sure you carry out a fair test. If you can, put your results into a table.

Weights are placed on the middle of the beam

The wooden beam rests on books or blocks at each end

The amount by which the beam bends is measured with a ruler

When you have finished, write a short article (perhaps on a word processor) telling people what they could do to make sure their own shelves do not bend.

2 Each picture shows a diving board. There are slight differences between the pictures.
a) What makes a diving board bend when someone stands on it?
b) Which of these diving boards would bend most when a person stood on it? Why?
c) Which diving board would bend least when the person stood on it? Why?

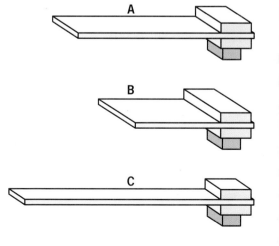

A

B

C

Strength

If the deforming forces acting on materials are too big, then the material may snap or break. If you bend a ruler with too much force, for example, it will snap. If you pull too hard on a rubber band it will break. Even your bones will break if the force is big enough.

Most things are designed so that they will not break or snap when they are in normal use. The materials used, and their size and shape, affect the **strength**.

Strong things can stand up to large forces. Weak things break when even small forces act on them.

Making things strong

To make things strong, we must use the right materials. The materials must also be put together in just the right way.

Ropes and steel cables are made up from many separate strands which are twisted together. The cables on a suspension bridge are made like this. Where really strong ropes are needed, such as those used to hold ships, several thinner ropes may be plaited together.

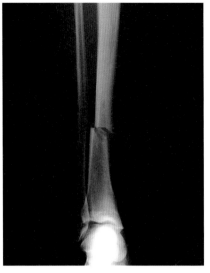
Bones are very strong but even the thickest bones can break

Carrier bags should be strong enough to hold the groceries

The steel cables must be strong enough to hold the bridge and the cars

The stool is designed to be strong, but also light. Some parts hold others together

Many strands are twisted together in cables and ropes

Plaiting rope makes it even stronger

To test the strength of cables and ropes they are pulled until they snap. Machines are used to exert large forces. The forces are often several thousand, or even several million, newtons.

Testing the strength of cable

★ THINGS TO DO

1 You can find the force needed to break things by pulling on them with a forcemeter. Another way is to hang weights on the material until it snaps. The weight hanging when the material breaks is equal to the force needed to break it.

Use one of these methods to find the force needed to:
   a) snap a thin (dry) twig,
   b) snap a thicker (dry) twig,
   c) snap some cotton (thread),
   d) tear a sheet of paper.

2 Ask your teacher to show you how to plait strands of wool. Do a test to find out whether plaited wool is stronger than twisted strands of wool. Put your results into a table and draw a series of pictures describing what you did. You could add a caption for each picture.

3 If fishing line is too weak it will snap when a fish is caught. The makers of fishing line must add a label describing how strong the line is.

Test 3 or 4 different fishing lines to find out which is strongest. Keep a note of any measurements you make and put them in a table when you have finished. Write a sentence saying which fishing line is strongest. Use your results to prove what you say.

4 Some pupils tested different types of cotton to find out which was strongest. The table shows their results.

Cotton	Weight needed to snap it
A	19 N
B	25 N
C	15 N
D	35 N

You can use a calculator to help you with these questions.
a) Which cotton needed 25 N to snap it?
b) Cotton A needed 19 N to snap it. How much more weight did cotton B hold before it snapped?
c) If B and D were used together, how much weight do you think they would hold?
d) The pupils drew this chart showing their results.

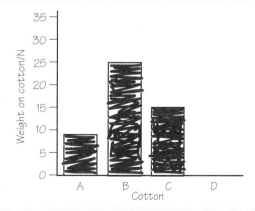

i) One of the bars is the wrong length. Which one is it? Draw the chart properly.
ii) Draw a bar on the chart for cotton D.

Don't slip!

If you could see the surface of things through a microscope you would notice that all surfaces are quite rough. Some, such as the surface of sandpaper, are very rough. Others, such as glass, are much smoother.

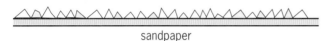

sandpaper

glass

The particles make the surface of sandpaper rough. Glass is much smoother

If you rub your finger over sandpaper you will feel the surface pushing against your finger. The force that pushes against your finger is called **friction**. Because glass is smoother there is less friction so your finger slides over it more easily.

It is friction between the soles of your shoes and the ground that stops you slipping. The rough soles and the rough ground grip one another so you do not slip.

The two rough surfaces grip one another, causing friction

On wet or icy paths the surface is much smoother. There is less friction. Because your shoes cannot grip the path properly you may slip. Wet or icy roads make driving difficult.

Many accidents happen in icy conditions

Cars take longer to stop because the tyres do not grip the ground so well. They may skid out of control. Drivers must take extra care under these conditions.

What a drag

The 'drag' on things that move through the air, or through liquids such as water, is friction. It is a force which acts against the movement. Like other forces, friction can affect the speed of moving objects. Imagine pedalling your bike along a level road.

friction

As you move, friction acts against you. If you exert sufficient force to balance out the friction force you will keep moving at a steady speed

If you exert a force that is bigger than the friction force, the extra force makes you speed up

If you stop pedalling, the only force acting on you is friction (pushing against your movement). This makes you slow down and eventually stop. If you pull on the brakes you create 'extra' friction (between the brake blocks and the wheels) so you slow down faster

★ THINGS TO DO

1 A group of pupils tried to find
out which trainers had the best
grip. They fired the shoes
across the floor using a rubber
band. They drew this picture
showing what they did.

a) What do you think they did
to make their tests 'fair'?

b) Their results table is shown.

i) Which shoe slid furthest across the floor?

ii) Which shoe slid 3.87 m across the floor?

iii) How much further than the *Blue Flash* did
the *White Light* slide?

d) Which trainer had the best grip?

e) Put the results into a bar chart.

Trainer	How far it slid
Blue Flash	2 metres and 67 centimetres
Red Thunder	4 metres and 5 centimetres
White Light	3 metres and 87 centimetres
Green Track	4 metres and 8 centimetres

2 Collect several different brands of trainers.
Design your own tests to find out which has the
best grip on the ground. You might get some
ideas from the pictures above and right.

When you have finished prepare a report
saying which shoe was best. Include any results
from your tests to prove what you say.

3 The grip between tyres and the road helps cars
and bikes to stop. You will find a chart like this in
The Highway Code. It shows how far cars travel
after braking at different speeds on dry roads.

a) How far will a car travelling at 30 mph (miles per hour) travel before stopping?

b) Why do you think the speed limit around town is 30 mph? Why can't it be higher?

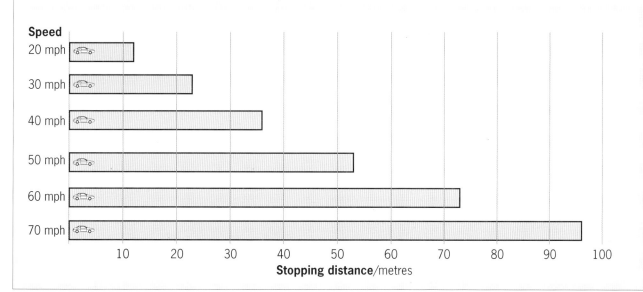

Tunnel or ferry?

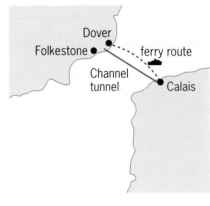

The channel tunnel was opened in 1995. Trains pass through the tunnel every hour carrying people, vans, lorries and coaches. The tunnel starts near Dover in England and ends near Calais in France. The journey takes 30 minutes.

Many people still prefer to travel from England to France by ferry. There is a ferry terminal at Dover. The ferry from Dover docks at Calais when it arrives in France. Although the journey is about the same distance, it takes an hour, that is 30 minutes longer than the train through the tunnel. That is because the train travels faster – it has a higher **speed**. It covers the same distance in a shorter time.

Speed, distance and time

Imagine two sprinters during a race. They start at the same time. The faster runner soon moves ahead of the slower one. He runs further in the same time.

At the end of the race, they will both have run the same distance. The faster runner will have completed the distance in less time. His speed was greater.

Drawing graphs

We could draw pictures to show how things move. Imagine a caterpillar crawling across the floor. We can draw 5 pictures showing how far it moved every 5 seconds. You can see from the pictures on the opposite page that:

- after 5 seconds the caterpillar had moved 10 cm,
- after 10 seconds the caterpillar had moved 20 cm,
- after 15 seconds the caterpillar had moved 30 cm,
- after 20 seconds the caterpillar had moved 40 cm,
- after 25 seconds the caterpillar had moved 50 cm.

| after 1 s | after 2 s | after 3 s | after 4 s | after 5 s |

We can plot the caterpillar's movement on a graph. One axis is drawn for distance travelled (the upright axis) and the other is for time taken (the horizontal axis).

Graphs such as this are called distance–time graphs because they show how far something has travelled (the distance) at any time.

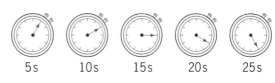

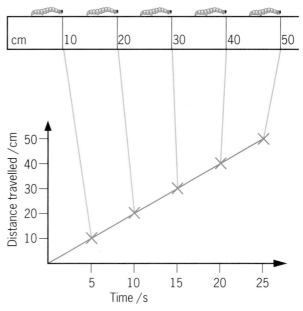

★ THINGS TO DO

1 The pictures show the speed of a tortoise, a crab and a hamster.

7 cm/s

5 cm/s

10 cm/s

a) If they raced over a 1 metre track, which would be the winner?
b) Which would be last home?

2 This diagram shows how to make a 'coke-can crawler'. Make one yourself.

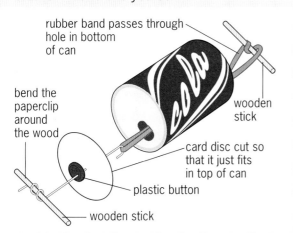

rubber band passes through hole in bottom of can

bend the paperclip around the wood

wooden stick

card disc cut so that it just fits in top of can

plastic button

wooden stick

Now hold the paper clip and wind the stick at the bottom of the can around and around, about 50 times. Without letting go of either the clip or the stick, place your crawler on the floor and then let go. It should move across the floor. If it does not, ask your teacher for help.

a) Measure how far your crawler moves in 2 seconds.

b) Find out how long it takes your crawler to move 1 metre.
c) Make a table with these headings in your notebook.

How long from the start   How far the crawler moved

Now do some tests to measure how far the crawler moves in 1 second, then in 2, 3, 4 and 5 seconds. Put your measurements into your table.
d) Draw these axes on some graph paper.

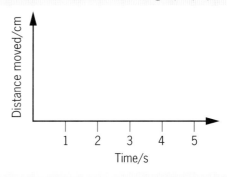

Plot a distance–time graph showing how your crawler moved, using the results from your table.

Package tour to space

Although this advert may sound silly, it may well be true in 20 or 30 years' time. The travel brochure could look like this:

★ 14 Days in Space! ★

★ Free transport to the rocket launch site ★

★ Free insurance ★

Full board with views over the seas and oceans of the world!

★ See your travel agent now for details of our new holiday destination ★

Day 1

Comfortable coach travel from your hotel to our rocket launch site where you can meet your fellow travellers over lunch.

Then it's all aboard our 5 star space shuttle, and soon we will blast off for our orbiting Space Hotel!

Once off the ground, settle down for the flight. At a height of about 800 km the shuttle will be free of the rocket and will join the Space Hotel in just under an hour. Fully trained staff travel with you to deal with any minor problems during the flight.

On arrival at the hotel our tour guides will be over the Moon to meet you!

After settling into your comfortable accommodation and enjoying a welcoming dinner you can have a peaceful night's sleep (even though we move from day into night 12 times each 24 hours!).

Sights to see during your stay
The surface of the Earth can be seen clearly from the panoramic windows in every room. Here we see a view of Europe from room D23.

Each time we pass over the North Pole (every 2 hours), you will see that the Earth has rotated beneath you on its daily journey.

Because we are above the Earth's atmosphere we can see the Moon (and other things) much more clearly. The Moon's craters will appear clearer than you have ever seen them before.

Weather satellites keep an eye on the Earth. By sending pictures of changing weather patterns back to Earth they help weather forecasters predict what the weather will be in different areas.

The Hubble Space Telescope (above) was launched into orbit in 1990 to provide clearer pictures than telescopes on Earth, which have difficulty seeing through pollution in the air. The picture above right shows a Hubble photograph of new stars being formed in the Eagle nebula, several thousand million million kilometres from Earth. The 'fingers' emerging from the pillar of hydrogen gas and dust are embryonic stars. Outside the nebula bright young stars can be seen.

Optional tour

For an extra 20 000 Euros you can join us on one of our walks into space! Here you will need to wear a special suit and oxygen is provided. For safety reasons we must insist that you remain tied to the space station at all times!

At the end of your stay

After breakfast on day 14 you will leave the Space Hotel by shuttle and will arrive back at the launch site within an hour.

You will then return to your Earth hotel by coach.

| Package cost, including flight, insurance, transfer, full board | 140 000 Euros |
| Optional space walk | 20 000 Euros |

★ THINGS TO DO

1 Space rockets use liquid fuel to 'blast off'. A water rocket works in a similar way. Ask your teacher to show you how a water rocket works.

Use a stopwatch to measure how long the rocket is in the air. Does the amount of time it stays in the air depend on how many pumps of air are put into it? Do a test to find out.

Write a report describing your tests and say what your measurements mean.

2 The United States hopes to send a manned spacecraft to Mars in the year 2000. It will carry 2 or 3 people and the journey there and back is expected to last 2 years.

Imagine you are planning this mission. What needs to be taken on the spacecraft? What problems might there be?

3 Many travel brochures show bar charts with the average temperature and hours of sunshine. Use the information in the table on page 65 to help you do the tasks below.
a) Draw a bar chart showing the surface temperatures on each planet in the solar system.
b) Draw a second bar chart showing the number of hours of daylight on each planet (you might need help with this one).

4 Use your research skills to find out as much as you can about how satellites are used.

Produce a handout for others in your class about satellites and their uses. Include some pictures.

Mars is over 230 million kilometres from Earth (about 150 million miles)

The solar system

The solar system is the group of planets, and their moons, that move around (orbit) the Sun. There are 9 planets, including the Earth, in the solar system. The orbits of the planets are not quite circular – more like squashed circles, with the Sun fairly close to the centre. Looking down on them from above our North Pole they all appear to move anticlockwise.

The Sun is huge – far, far bigger than anything else in the solar system. The Sun and the Earth pull on one another. The pulling force is **gravity**. Gravity stops us spinning away into outer space. Gravity also holds all the other planets in orbit around the Sun. It takes the Earth just over 365 days (1 year) to travel once around the Sun. Venus and Mercury, because they are closer to the Sun, take less time. The other planets, which are further away from the Sun than the Earth, take longer because they have further to travel and are slower.

The planets in our solar system (not to scale)

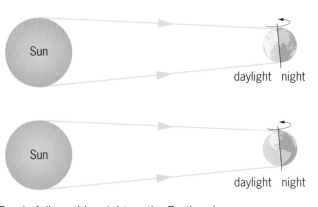

Day is followed by night as the Earth spins

In a spin

As the Earth orbits the Sun, it also spins around itself (on its own axis). It spins once every 24 hours. At any time one half of the Earth faces the Sun. That half is in daylight. The opposite half faces away from the Sun – it is in darkness.

Some planets take longer than 24 hours to spin around once. Venus, for example, takes about 243 days, which means daylight would last about 120 Earth days, followed by 120 days of darkness! This does not really happen, because Venus is covered by clouds that are too thick to let much light pass through.

Live from Australia

The first satellite to orbit the Earth was the Russian *Sputnik.* It was launched in 1957. The gravity force between the Earth and the satellite kept it in orbit. Since then thousands of satellites have been launched.

Communications satellites are used to send TV pictures, telephone messages and computerised information all around the world.

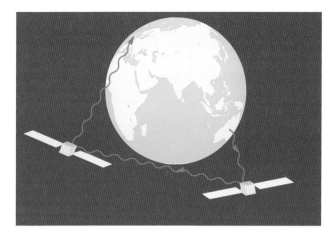

Signals sent via satellite travel so fast that viewers in the UK can see what is happening in Australia 'as it happens'

★ THINGS TO DO

1 The table below shows some information about the planets in the solar system.

Planet	Distance from **Sun**/millions of km	Average surface temperature /°C	Time to spin once on its axis	Time to travel once around the **Sun**/years
Mercury	58	350	1416 h	0.24
Venus	108	460	5832 h	0.6
Earth	150	15	24 h	1
Mars	228	−25	24 h 37 min	1.9
Jupiter	779	−120	9 h 56 min	11.9
Saturn	1427	−180	10 h 20 min	29.5
Uranus	2670	−200	10 h 50 min	84
Neptune	4496	−220	15 h 50 min	165
Pluto	5906	−240	154 h	248

a) Choose one of the planets and describe how day and night would be different from that on Earth.

b) Suppose another planet was discovered 5000 million km from the Sun. About how long do you think it would take to orbit the Sun?

c) Imagine that another planet was found 3500 million km from the Sun. What do you think its surface temperature might be?

2 Use your research skills to collect as much information as you can about each of the planets in the solar system. You may be able to use the library, CD-ROMs or other computer information systems.

Design your own computer database containing information about the planets of our solar system.

You could also produce an instruction booklet (using a word processor) so that other people can use your database.

Man in the Moon?

The surface of the Moon

Meteorites have formed craters on the Earth's surface, similar to those on the Moon

The Moon, because it travels around the Earth, is a natural satellite.

The craters on the Moon's surface were formed by meteorites (lumps of rock which hurtle through space) smashing into the surface. Some craters are many miles across, suggesting they were formed by massive meteorites travelling very fast.

Some people believe that much of the surface of the Earth originally looked like that of the Moon. Over millions of years the craters have been worn down by the Earth's weather.

The Moon takes just over 27 days to orbit the Earth. It is held in orbit by the large gravity force between the Earth and itself. Without the gravity force, the Moon would shoot off into space.

The Moon does not produce its own light – it is lit by the Sun. Occasionally the Earth passes exactly between the Sun and the Moon. The sunlight which would normally fall on the Moon is blocked off by the Earth.

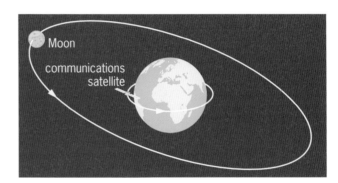

The Moon's orbit

The Earth's shadow on the Moon during an eclipse of the Moon

The first people to land on the Moon were the American astronauts Neil Armstrong and Buzz Aldrin in 1969. On later Moon missions astronauts took small electricity-powered buggies which allowed them to travel across the Moon's surface. (They're still there if you want to go and collect them!)

They saw the Sun rising over the Earth in a quite different way.

Edwin (Buzz) Aldrin on the Moon with the Lunar Excursion Module

The Earth photographed by the crew of an Apollo moon mission

★ THINGS TO DO

1 The craters on the Moon are thought to have been caused by meteorites striking the surface. You can model this using ball-bearings and sand.

a) Drop a ball-bearing into some sand in a tray. What pattern does the ball-bearing make? Does it leave a crater like those on the Moon?

b) Do you think the height from which the ball-bearing is dropped will affect the size of the crater? What do you think will happen if you drop it from (i) higher, (ii) lower?

c) Test your ideas. Keep a record of any measurements you make. Try to put them into a table.

d) What do your results tell you? Show your results to others. Do they agree with you?

2 Make a model of the Sun and the Earth like this.

a) The Earth spins on itself. Turn the globe slowly around. Which part of the Earth is just coming into 'daylight'? Which part is in darkness?

b) Now turn the globe through half a turn. Where is the part of the Earth which was coming into daylight earlier? What has happened to the part that was in darkness?

c) Make a poster (for a primary school) which shows them why the Earth has periods of day and night.

How it all began

Out there in space there are at least 10 000 million million million stars! Our Sun is a star. It looks much bigger and much brighter than any other star because it is very much closer to us. Between the stars there is dust, ice and gas. There may even be other planets and their moons.

The space that all of these stars take up is called the Universe. No-one really knows how big the Universe is. No-one is really sure whether the ideas shown in science fiction films such as *Star Trek*, of other Universes beyond our own, are true. What we are fairly sure of is that forces played a large part in the formation of the Universe and everything in it.

How was the Universe made?

One idea is that everything started as a very dense mixture of many different particles held together by gravity.

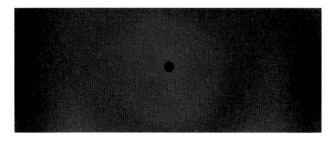

About 16 thousand million years ago it exploded. The explosion – called the 'Big Bang' – was enormous, far bigger than anything we can imagine.

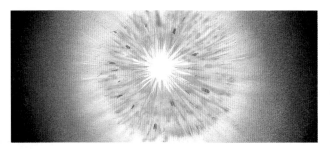

The explosion created a huge fireball which spread very quickly. Its temperature was probably over 100 thousand million °C. For millions of years material from the Big Bang spread out through space.

Huge clouds of hydrogen gas formed in some places. Gravity pulled the particles of hydrogen gas closer together. The clouds got smaller and hotter, and began to produce light. These were the first stars.

Gravity forces pulled the stars towards one another, too. In some places there were more stars than others. Huge **galaxies** (places where millions of stars gathered together) were formed. There may now be as many as 100 000 million galaxies in the Universe, each containing as many as 100 000 million stars.

Where are we in the Universe?

The Earth lies in a galaxy called the Milky Way. It is so big that it would take 1 million million years to go from one side of the Milky Way to the other if we travelled at 100 kilometres per hour! If we could see the Milky Way from 'outside' it would look like a big spiral made up of millions of stars. Most of the stars are in the arms of the spiral. Our Sun is one of these stars.

The galaxies in the Universe are millions and millions of kilometres apart. The nearest galaxy to our own is the Andromeda galaxy, which is over 2 million million million kilometres away. Travelling at the speed of light (300 000 kilometres per second) it would take over 2 million years to reach it!

The Milky Way is a spiral galaxy

The Andromeda galaxy

★ THINGS TO DO

1 Many people read their 'stars' in the newspaper. The star signs or 'signs of the zodiac' are really names of constellations – groups of stars with special shapes.

Aries The ram	**Libra** The scales
Taurus The bull	**Scorpio** The scorpion
Gemini The twins	**Sagittarius** The archer
Cancer The crab	**Capricorn** The goat
Leo The lion	**Aquarius** The water carrier
Virgo The woman	**Pisces** The fish

The signs of the zodiac

These pictures show the positions of the stars in some of the constellations. Copy them and join the stars with lines to form a picture of the shape of the constellation. Which signs of the zodiac do you think they are?

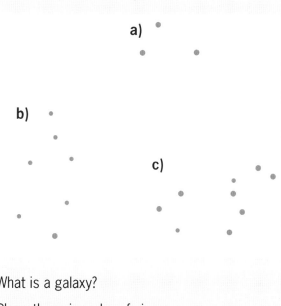

2 What is a galaxy?

3 Place these in order of size:
solar system, planet, Universe, galaxy.

Drawing line graphs

If the thing you changed during your investigation is described by a number then you should draw a line graph using your results (see page 20). The results shown in the table below were gathered during an investigation to find out whether the speed of a chemical reaction was affected by the temperature at which the reaction took place. Let's see how we can draw a line graph using the results.

Temperature/°C	Time to collect 50 cm³ of gas/s
20	108
30	89
40	70
50	48
60	30

This is what was changed during the investigation. These numbers always go on the horizontal axis

This is what was measured each time the temperature was changed. These values go on the vertical axis

Notice that the lowest and the highest values on the axes are chosen so that they are just below the smallest value in each column and just above the highest value. Sometimes you might need to start your axes at 0

Notice also that each axis is labelled with a description and units for the numbers

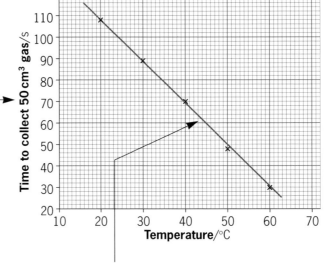

The line does not go from point to point – a line is drawn that passes in the region of most of the points. This is called a 'line of best fit'. (On some graphs the line might be a curve – you must decide on the best shape for your line)

★ **THINGS TO DO**

Draw a line graph using these results.

Weight on diving board/N	Amount the board bends/cm
200	25
400	35
600	44
800	56
1000	63

4

WAVES AND RADIATION

Deafening

At a pop concert large loudspeakers make sure that even those who are furthest away can hear the sound. Some people even claim that the sound can be heard several streets away from the concert! (Lucky them – they do not have to buy a ticket.)

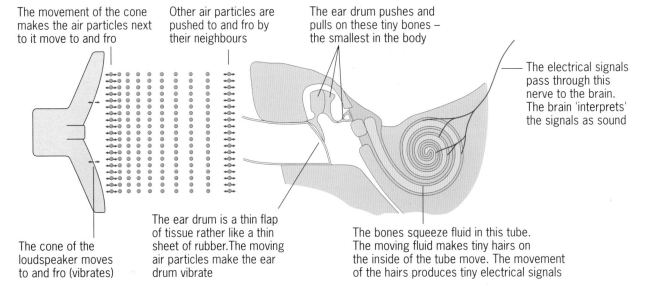

The movement of the cone makes the air particles next to it move to and fro

Other air particles are pushed to and fro by their neighbours

The ear drum pushes and pulls on these tiny bones – the smallest in the body

The electrical signals pass through this nerve to the brain. The brain 'interprets' the signals as sound

The cone of the loudspeaker moves to and fro (vibrates)

The ear drum is a thin flap of tissue rather like a thin sheet of rubber. The moving air particles make the ear drum vibrate

The bones squeeze fluid in this tube. The moving fluid makes tiny hairs on the inside of the tube move. The movement of the hairs produces tiny electrical signals

How do you hear?

Sound is carried from a loudspeaker to your ear by air particles. The to-and-fro movement of the air particles makes your ear drum vibrate. Inside the ear, vibrations are turned into tiny electrical signals which pass through nerves to your brain.

The movement of the air particles is a **sound wave**. The sound wave carries energy from the loudspeaker to your ear. *Waves pass energy from one place to another.*

Notice that the vibrations of the air particles are parallel to (in line with) the direction in which the wave carries energy. This kind of wave is called a **longitudinal wave**. All sound waves are longitudinal waves.

Sound waves can be reflected from hard objects, such as a wall. The waves which 'bounce back' are called echoes. Soft materials, such as curtains or carpets, absorb (soak up) most of the sound rather than reflecting it.

Protect your hearing

Loud sounds from pop concerts produce big vibrations in the air. These big vibrations can affect your hearing for several hours afterwards. Regular exposure to loud sounds can cause permanent damage.

The loudness of sounds is measured in **decibels** (**dB**) by a sound-level meter. The loudness of some common sounds, compared with a sound that is just loud enough to be heard, is shown in the chart below.

Sounds of 80 dB and over cause pain as the ear drum is overstretched. Sounds above 140 dB cause permanent damage to the ears, resulting in deafness. Precautions are taken to protect the hearing of workers in noisy places.

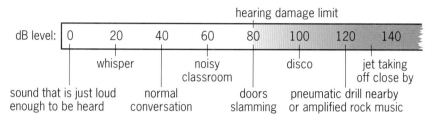

★ **THINGS TO DO**

1 Some homes, especially those near major roads, have sound-proofing materials placed in the walls. Think about how you could test a range of materials to find out which would be best to use as sound-proofing. You could try polystyrene, loft insulation, cotton wool, foam rubber, or even scraps of clothing.
(Hint: you could use a tape recorder, or a sound-level meter.)

2 The bar charts on the right show the loudness of sounds produced by different tracks on two CDs.
a) Which track produced the loudest sound on CD 1?
b) Which was the quietest track on CD 2?
c) Which track, on which CD, produced the loudest sound of all?
d) Why would it be unfair to say that CD 2 was the most likely to damage your hearing?

3 Some pupils measured the loudness of sound at different distances from a hi-fi speaker. They drew this graph using their results.
a) What connection is there between the loudness and how far you are from a speaker?
b) How far should you sit from this speaker to avoid temporary hearing damage? (Use the chart on the opposite page to help you.)
c) Draw another graph showing what would happen if the volume was turned down.

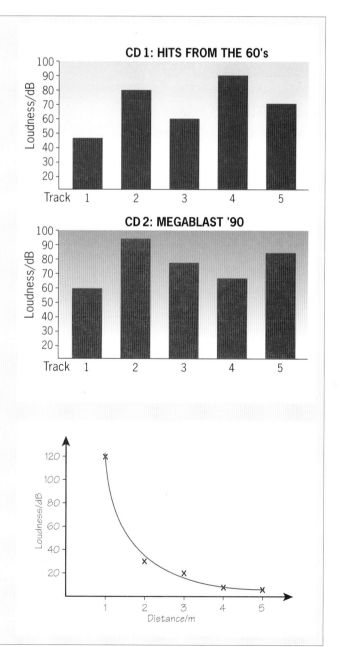

Let's make a row!

We can recognise millions of different sounds. Perhaps surprisingly, all sounds are produced in much the same way – by something moving to-and-fro, or vibrating. This busker's instruments produce different sounds.

The vibrations from the instruments (or the crashing together of the cymbals) make the air particles vibrate. The air particles then carry the sound to our ears. The pattern of vibrations from each instrument is different, so the musical sounds are different. The crashing sound from the cymbals might be referred to as 'noise'.

Inside the voice box (the larynx) thin strips of tissue (the vocal cords) vibrate as air is forced over them

The mouth organ contains thin strips of metal which vibrate

When struck, the drumskin vibrates to and fro

The cymbals crash together

The guitar strings vibrate when the are plucked

Picturing waves

An oscilloscope can be used to create a 'picture' that shows the pattern of vibrations in the air. The 'picture' is really a graph showing how the air pressure changes as the sound wave passes. It is not a picture of the sound wave itself.

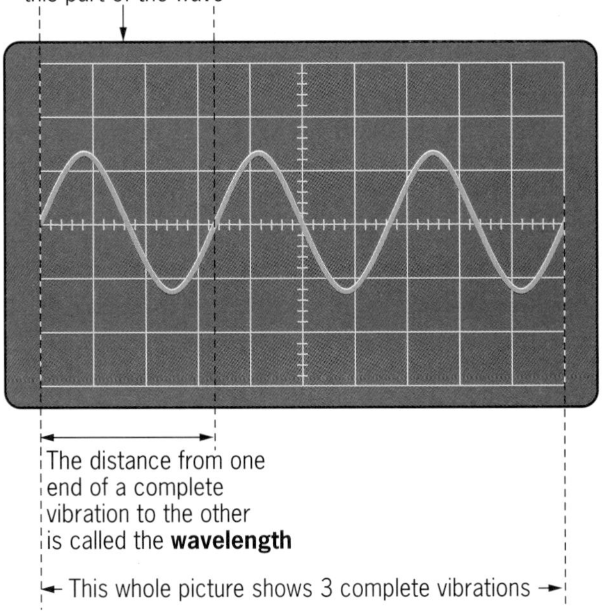

High and low

The keys on the left-hand side of a piano produce low notes. We say they have a **low pitch**. The keys on the right-hand side produce higher notes. We say they have a **high pitch**. The 'wave pictures' of the notes at the top of the next page show why they sound different.

You can see that as you play the notes from left to right, the vibrations of the sound get closer and closer together.

A single vibration of the air particles produces this part of the wave

The distance from one end of a complete vibration to the other is called the **wavelength**

← This whole picture shows 3 complete vibrations →

The **wave frequency** (the number of vibrations each second) increases. You can also see that as the frequency increases the wavelength gets smaller.

The notes sound different because the frequency of the vibrations has changed.

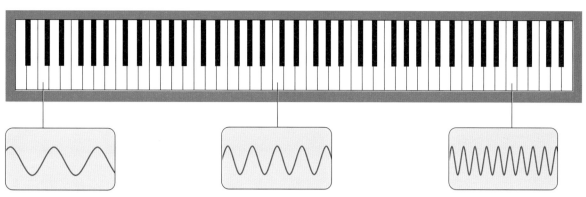

The vibrations of a low-pitch note are quite far apart. They have a low frequency

This note has a higher pitch. The vibrations are closer together. They have a higher frequency

This note has an even higher pitch. The vibrations are very close together. They have an even higher frequency

Louder sounds

Sound waves are energy carriers. Loud sounds carry more energy so make bigger vibrations in the air. On a 'wave picture' we would see that the height of the wave – the **amplitude** – gets bigger as the sound gets louder.

Can you hear it?

Most humans can hear a wide range of frequencies. The lowest sound that most people hear has about 20 vibrations each second – a frequency of 20 **hertz (Hz)**.

High-pitched notes are produced by things that vibrate much more quickly. The highest sound you are likely to hear is one that produces about 20 000 vibrations each second – a frequency of 20 000 Hz.

Quiet sounds give small amplitude waves

Louder sounds give waves with a larger amplitude

The wings of the bumble bee are vibrating about 25 times each second, producing a low-pitched note

Some animals can hear sounds that we cannot hear. Sound with frequencies too high for us to hear is called **ultrasound**. Ultrasound waves are produced by things that vibrate very quickly – more than 20 000 times each second.

Bats, flying at night, cannot see in the dark. The bat sends out an ultrasound wave. The wave is reflected by solid objects in its path.

When the bat receives the 'echo' its brain works out the distance and position of the reflecting object. The bat knows exactly where things are!

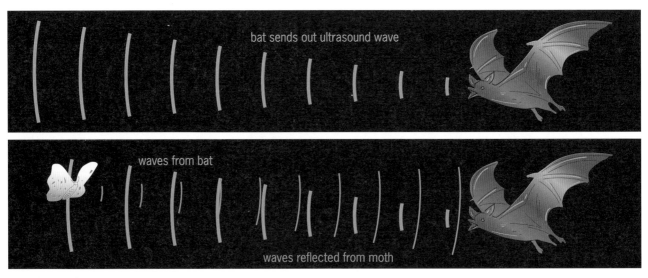

Bats locate their prey by ultrasound

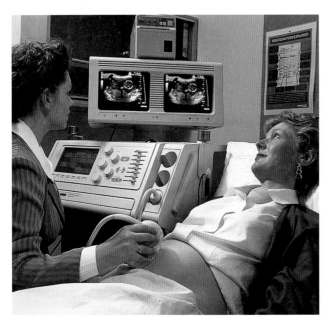

We can use ultrasound

When doctors need to check on unborn babies they use ultrasound. (X-rays cannot be used as they might harm the baby.) The reflected ultrasound waves are processed by a computer, which turns them into a picture of the baby in the womb. The doctors can tell how well it is growing, and can identify any problems long before the baby is due to be born.

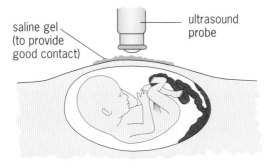

An ultrasound scan

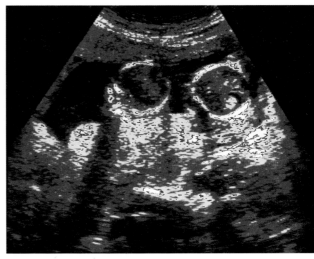

Ultrasound scan image showing twins

Ultrasound can also be used for cleaning items that could not easily be washed, such as the reflectors in street lights, and for cleaning delicate fabrics without damage. The very high frequency of the ultrasound vibrations 'shakes' the dirt away. Dentists may also use ultrasound to 'shake' the hard coating of tartar from your teeth, helping to prevent gum disease.

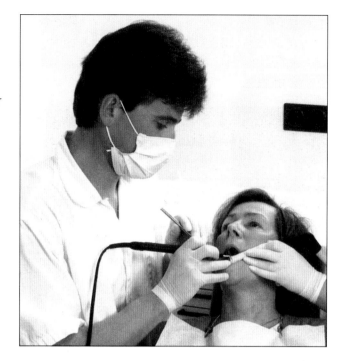

Ultrasound vibrations can clean tartar from teeth

★ THINGS TO DO

1 You can find garden chimes on sale in many garden centres. As the wind blows the chimes sound.

a) Do some tests to find out if there is any connection between the length of the metal cylinders and the pitch of the note they produce (how high or low it sounds).
b) If possible find out whether the type of metal affects the note.
c) Try to produce a short tune on a set of chimes. Write your music down in a way that others can use to play your tune.

2 This picture shows part of an instrument called a xylophone. It has wooden bars of different lengths which produce notes when they are tapped. Each bar is numbered. Number 2, for example, produces a 'D' note.

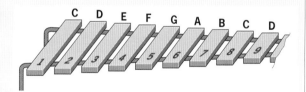

Hap-py Birth-day to you Hap-py Birth-day to you

The music is for the song 'Happy Birthday'. Change the music into a list of numbers (those on the xylophone) that could be used by a child to play the tune.

Visible light

Light carries energy 150 million km from the Sun to the Earth. The energy is carried by a special kind of wave called an **electromagnetic wave**. There are many different types of electromagnetic wave. Light is the only one that we can see.

Reflections

Light is reflected from most smooth, shiny surfaces. This allows you to see things even when you may not be looking directly at them, and also to see yourself!

By arranging a mirror at just the right angle we can see things that are behind us, or to the side of us.

Drivers need to know whether other vehicles are approaching them from behind

Sometimes more than one mirror is used. A simple periscope, for example, changes the direction of light twice using two mirrors.

Each mirror reflects the light through 90°. The light emerges at a different level to that at which it entered the periscope

Notice that the angle at which the ray strikes the mirror is the same as the angle at which it is reflected from the mirror. This is the case for all mirrors.

Some mirrors are curved. The curved mirror in this picture allows the shop assistant to see what is happening behind the shelves.

Other curved mirrors can concentrate light.

A spotlight uses a curved reflector to concentrate the light on one place

A floodlight spreads the light over a wider area. Floodlight reflectors are less curved than spotlight reflectors

★ THINGS TO DO

1 Winalot United need new floodlights but can't afford too many. They need lights that will spread light over a wide area of the pitch (but still be bright).

Do some tests to find out:

a) how the shape of the reflector behind the bulb affects how much the light spreads out after it is reflected;

b) whether the height of the light above the ground affects how much the light spreads out.

Write a letter suggesting how they can get the best floodlighting on their ground.

2 The wing mirrors on a car are flat (plane) mirrors. The driver adjusts the angle of the mirrors to see what is alongside the car.

Copy these pictures into your notebook. Draw where the reflected rays would go.

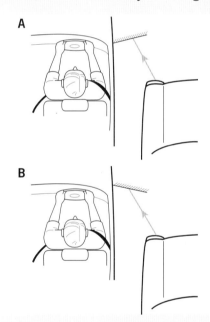

Which position of the mirror is better for the driver to see cars alongside?

3 A shopkeeper needs a mirror in the corner of the shop so that he can see 'behind' the shelves.

Test different mirrors to find out which one will 'see' over the biggest angle (so that he can see most of this shop).

Keep a record of your results so that you can show which is best.

Refracting light

Normally light travels in a straight line from place to place. Light travelling to you from a street light in the distance travels in a straight line. Sometimes, however, light changes direction. When light goes into your eye, its direction is changed so that the light rays form a picture, or image, at just the right place – on the retina at the back of your eye.

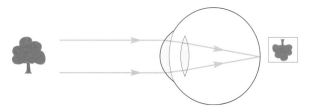

The light rays change direction as they go from one layer of your eye into another

Some people cannot see clearly because the image is not formed on the retina. For example, for a short-sighted person things in the distance are blurred.

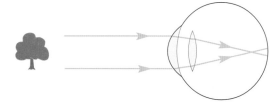

The image is formed in front of the retina

To correct the problem a lens is placed in front of the eye. The lens changes the direction of the rays so that the eye can form the image on the retina. The person will then see clearly.

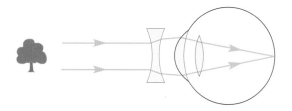

A correcting lens changes the direction of the light rays

Light passes more easily through some materials than through others. It may speed up or slow down as it goes from one material to another. Sometimes this causes its direction to change, as you have seen above. The change in direction is called **refraction**.

All the colours of the rainbow

Sunlight is a mixture of colours that we cannot normally see because the colours are mixed up. When the light is refracted (for example, as it passes through a layer of moisture) the colours separate so that they can be clearly seen. The 7 colours – red, orange, yellow, green, blue, indigo, violet – are known as the **spectrum of white light**. The effect of splitting up the white light into these colours is called **dispersion**.

A rainbow is formed when sunlight is refracted and reflected by raindrops in the air

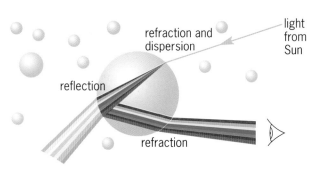

Colour and wavelength

The different colours are all electromagnetic waves (see page 82) with slightly different wavelengths. Red light, for example, has a longer wavelength than green light. As we move through the spectrum from red to violet the wavelength gets smaller.

Coloured materials contain chemicals called pigments. There are many different pigments which reflect and absorb different colours. A red jumper, for example, reflects red light but absorbs most others. A green jumper reflects the green light but absorbs most others.

The cells of your retinas and your brain, working together, see the different wavelengths as different 'colours'. Some animals cannot see colours – they see only in black and white.

white light

Red light waves have a longer wavelength than green light waves

---

★ THINGS TO DO

1 a) Put a glass block on a piece of white paper. Draw a line around the block with a pencil.
b) Now put a ray box on the paper so that a single ray of light strikes the side of the block.
c) Draw along the ray of light to where it hits the block.
d) Draw along the ray which comes out of the other side of the block.

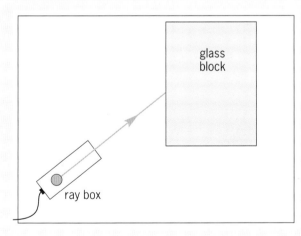
glass block

ray box

e) Take everything off the paper and draw a line (using a ruler) connecting the ray going into the block and the one leaving the block.
f) Copy the drawing into your notebook and describe how the ray changes direction. Note particularly which way the direction changes at each surface.

g) Now set up the block as shown in each of these diagrams (one at a time) and repeat your experiment.

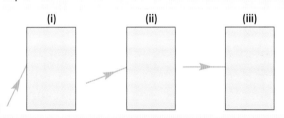
(i) (ii) (iii)

h) Write a sentence saying what the experiments tell you about refraction.

2 Shine the light from a ray box onto the side of a prism like this.

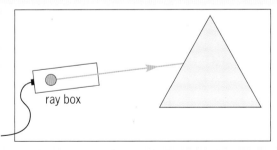
ray box

a) Draw a picture showing how the ray passes through the prism and out the other side.
b) What happens to its direction as it goes into the prism?
c) What happens to its direction as it leaves the prism?

The electromagnetic spectrum

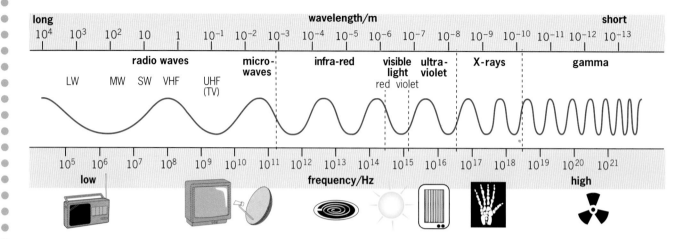

There are many types of electromagnetic wave. The chart above shows the **electromagnetic spectrum** – a sort of league table of electromagnetic waves!

Notice how the wavelengths get shorter as you go from left to right, while the frequencies (how many wave vibrations there are each second) get higher.

All of these waves:

- transfer energy from place to place;
- are **transverse waves** – the vibrations are at right angles to the direction in which energy is transferred;
- travel at the same speed (about 300 thousand km every second);
- can be reflected and refracted.

Radio station	Wavelength	Frequency
Radio 1	3 m	99.8 MHz
Radio Scotland	370 m	810 kHz
Radio 4	1565 m	198 kHz
Radio 5	330 m	909 kHz

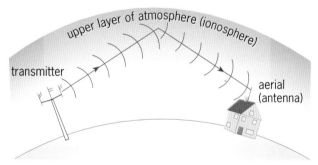

Longer wavelength radio waves can be reflected from the ionosphere

Radio and TV waves

Radio (and TV) waves are the longest waves in the electromagnetic spectrum. The waves that carry the signals from different broadcasting stations have different wavelengths and frequencies.

Long-wavelength radio waves (such as Radio 4) can reflect off a layer in the atmosphere (the ionosphere), allowing people who live a long way from the transmitter to listen to the radio station.

Satellite TV

Microwaves are very short-wavelength radio waves. They pass through the atmosphere easily, so are used for satellite communications. The satellite acts as a link, receiving signals from one part of the world and then transmitting them down to different places (see page 65).

Satellite dishes collect the microwave signals from the satellite and reflect them to the end of the arm (the transducer).

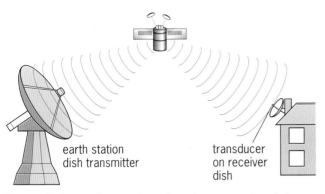

earth station
dish transmitter

transducer
on receiver
dish

Transmission and reception of a microwave signal via satellite

The shape of a satellite dish ensures that lots of microwave energy is concentrated on the transducer

---

★ THINGS TO DO

This information was found in a book about microwave ovens.

A microwave is a short wave /\/\/\/\/ (transverse waveform) rather like a radio wave but shorter.

Microwaves are reflected by metal, but they pass through materials such as glass, paper, plastic and Pyrex without heating them.

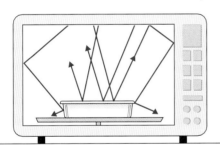

Metal materials reflect microwaves

Microwave ovens produce a particular wavelength which is absorbed by water molecules. Because the water in food absorbs energy, it gets hotter. It then warms other surrounding food particles. Heat then passes through the rest of the food.

microwave energy is absorbed by the water molecules

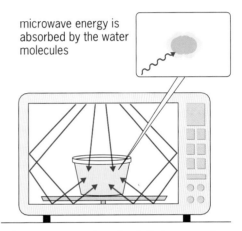

When microwaves pass into food, their energy is absorbed by the water molecules, raising the temperature and cooking the food

Microwaves penetrate about 4 cm into food from the outside. If food is thicker than 8 cm the centre will cook by conduction rather than by direct microwave radiation.

To sum up, microwaves penetrate food, creating quick heat, but they will not directly heat the oven cavity or the container. This makes for fast, economic cooking.

a) Which of the following materials can microwaves pass through, and which reflect microwaves? Make a table.
  kitchen roll, kitchen foil, polystyrene food container, glass dish, metal can, plastic dish
b) Why can't take-away foods served in metal foil containers be reheated in a microwave oven?
c) What makes food heat up in a microwave oven?

Sunburn can be dangerous

You can be badly burned if you sunbathe for too long. The Sun's rays contain a form of electromagnetic radiation called **ultra-violet** (or **UV**), which, like infra-red and microwaves, cannot be seen. It is ultra-violet radiation that makes our skin tan, but shorter wavelengths of the ultra-violet radiation are dangerous.

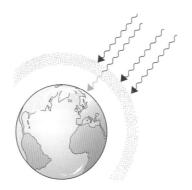

The ozone layer prevents most of the dangerous ultra-violet radiation reaching the Earth

In some places the ozone layer has become thinner. More of the dangerous radiation is reaching the Earth

If too much short-wavelength ultra-violet radiation reaches the Earth it could:

- cause skin cancer;
- cause eye damage;
- damage the immune system (which fights infection in the body);
- cause trees and plants to grow more slowly, or cause stunted growth.

A natural sun filter

A gas called ozone, which is found between 15 and 40 km above the Earth, filters out most of the dangerous UV rays from the Sun. The **ozone layer**, as it is called, has helped to protect us from many of the dangers.

For the past 15 years or so, however, the amount of ozone in the atmosphere has been decreasing. The ozone is being destroyed by some kinds of pollution, especially by certain chemicals that are used in aerosol sprays. Some steps have been taken around the world to reduce the use of these chemicals. This should slow down damage to the ozone layer.

Who is most at risk?

Young children are generally exposed to much more UV than adults, because they play outside for long periods. Babies are particularly at risk of sunburn because they have thin skin. They are also more likely to suffer eye damage.

Sunscreen lotions contain chemicals that filter out the harmful wavelengths of the UV. Generally, the higher the 'filter factor', the more UV they filter out – and the less chance of sunburn.

By protecting our skin in the first 18 years it is estimated that the risk of skin cancer decreases by 80%

Every time your skin is badly burned by the sun the risk of skin cancer increases. If you have light (fair) skin you are more likely to be sunburnt and you are more at risk of damage to deeper tissues, leading to cancer.

Uses of ultra-violet radiation

Because ultra-violet radiation damages living tissues it is often used in shops that sell fresh meat, fish and dairy products – the radiation kills any microbes and small insects that may be present.

UV lights are used to destroy microbes that would spoil fresh food

Some chemicals **fluoresce** when UV radiation falls on them – they absorb the UV and emit visible light. Security paints and markers contain fluorescent chemicals that cannot normally be seen, but are seen clearly when lit by UV.

Fluorescent security markers can be used to label things like hi-fis, enabling the police to return stolen items to the owners when they are recovered

Fluorescent strip lights produce UV light that could be harmful. They are coated with a chemical which absorbs the UV radiation. The chemical then emits safe white light as it glows.

★ THINGS TO DO

It is thought that some flower petals contain a chemical that reflects ultra-violet light. The chemicals form a pattern which can be seen by insects but not by us.

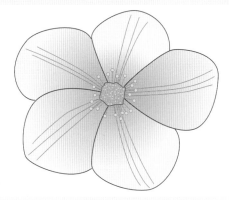

The patterns on the petals guide the insect to the parts of the flower that contain nectar

a) Make two flowers using coloured crepe or tissue paper. Draw a pattern on the petals of one using a security marker. The pattern will glow under a UV lamp if your school has one. On the other draw nothing.

> **WARNING:** Always wear safety glasses when working with UV light, and use the lamp only for a short time.

b) How could you find out whether insects follow the ultra-violet pattern? Do a test in the school grounds to find out.

Radioactivity

Inside some substances the atoms change, releasing fast electrically charged particles and possibly gamma rays (another type of electromagnetic wave). These substances are radioactive. The changes occurring in the atoms is called **radioactivity**.

Alpha radiation is a stream of positively charged particles. Although they travel at around 10 000 km per second, they are much slower than either beta particles or gamma waves. Alpha particles are easily absorbed by paper, and by the outer layers of your skin. They cause most damage if they get inside your body

Beta radiation is a stream of negatively charged particles – electrons. They are much lighter than alpha particles and travel faster. They can be absorbed by thin layers of metal foil

Gamma radiation is NOT particles – it is an electromagnetic wave. Travelling at the same speed as light, it penetrates most materials easily but is stopped by thick layers of lead and concrete

Background radiation

Many people do not realise that they are bombarded with ionising radiation every day.

The radiation from these sources is called **background radiation**. Although it does not seriously affect our health, that does not mean it does us no harm. Doctors and scientists believe that the more we are exposed to ionising radiation, the greater the risk.

Radioactive substances release **ionising radiation**. This is very dangerous because it can damage (or even kill) human cells. Three types of ionising radiation are emitted from radioactive substances – alpha, beta and gamma radiation. Some substances emit all three types. Others emit only one or two.

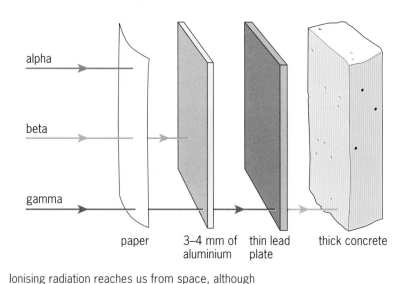

alpha

beta

gamma

paper   3–4 mm of aluminium   thin lead plate   thick concrete

Ionising radiation reaches us from space, although much of it is stopped by the atmosphere. People who fly regularly, such as pilots and flight attendants, absorb more of this cosmic radiation than others

Every minute we breathe in about 1000 radioactive particles! The radiation from them is absorbed by our lungs. Most of the particles in the air are released from the ground. A very small proportion comes from industry and nuclear power stations

Many foods (and drinks) contain small amounts of a substance called potassium-40. This is a very weakly radioactive substance. The potassium-40 changes inside your body, releasing ionising radiation. The kidneys carefully control the amount of potassium in the body (at safe levels) regardless of what we eat

Some rocks and building materials such as bricks emit gamma radiation which is absorbed by our bodies every day

What are the dangers?

Too much ionising radiation can cause cancer. Cancer cells are living cells that go out of control. They cannot then do their job properly. Very large amounts of ionising radiation may kill the cells altogether.

... and the uses?

Ionising radiation is used to:

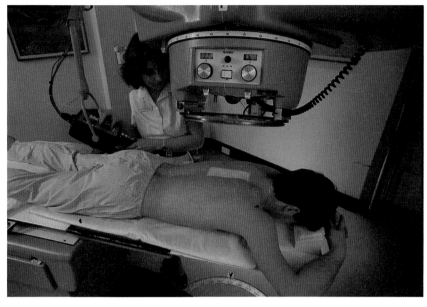

In radiotherapy, gamma radiation is used to destroy cancer cells

- destroy cancer cells in the body;
- identify problems in the body – radioactive 'tracers' are put into the body and a special detector tracks their movement through the part of the body being investigated;

- sterilise medical instruments by killing any organisms on the instruments;
- treat foods to kill organisms that cause spoilage;
- trace leaks in oil and gas pipes.

★ THINGS TO DO

1 This table shows how much background radiation we might receive from different sources.

Where the radiation comes from	How much
Radioactive gas released from underground rocks	51%
Hospitals and other medical uses	12%
From inside our bodies, due to eating, drinking and breathing	12%
Gamma rays from rocks, building materials and soil	14%
From space (cosmic radiation)	10%
Other sources	1%

Draw a pie chart using the information. You could use a colour key to label each sector.

2 Smoke alarms contain a small amount of radioactive material.

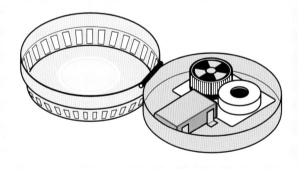

a) Are some alarms more sensitive than others? Test 2 or 3 different alarms to see how well they work. Show others what you find out.

b) The radioactive material in a smoke alarm gives off alpha radiation. Why is the alpha radiation unlikely to affect people's health?

Glossary

alpha radiation An ionising radiation consisting of positively charged particles, released from some radioactive substances

alternating current (a.c.) Electric current that pulses to and fro, changing direction regularly

ampere The unit of electric current, usually shortened to **amp**

amplitude A measure of the size of a wave disturbance, e.g. the loudness of a sound

background radiation The ionising radiation we are exposed to every day from sources all around us

beta radiation An ionising radiation consisting of fast-moving electrons, released from some radioactive substances

boiling point The temperature at which a liquid (e.g. water) boils (100 °C for water)

compression A material is in compression if it is being squashed

conduction (of heat energy) A method by which energy passes through a material, not involving the movement of atoms

conductor (of electricity) A material (metal or carbon) through which electric current can flow

conductor (of heat energy) A material through which energy passes by conduction. Metals are good conductors

convection A method by which energy spreads through a liquid or a gas, involving movement of the particles of the liquid or gas

current (electric) The flow of electrons through a conducting circuit

decibel The unit of perceived loudness of sounds, written as **dB**

direct current (d.c.) Electric current that flows in one direction

dispersion The separation of a mixture of electromagnetic waves into the constituent wavelengths. White light can be dispersed (separated) into the colours of the rainbow (the spectrum of white light)

dynamo A device that creates an electric current when mechanical work is done on it

efficient A device is efficient if most of the energy put in is changed or transferred in a useful way

elastic An elastic material springs back into shape after being deformed

electromagnet A magnet consisting of a piece of soft iron surrounded by coils of wire, whose magnetism can be switched on and off by switching a current supply to the coils on and off

electromagnetic wave Any type of wave that travels in the same way and at the same speed as visible light. Each type of electromagnetic wave has a different range of wavelengths/frequencies

energy The ability to do work

evaporation The escape of liquid molecules from the surface of a liquid, as vapour. This occurs at all temperatures

fluoresce When a substance fluoresces it absorbs ultra-violet radiation and emits visible light

force A push or a pull

fossil fuels Fuels (sources of energy) formed from the fossilised remains of living things: coal, oil and gas

freezing point The temperature at which a liquid (e.g. water) freezes (turns to ice: 0 °C for water)

frequency A measure of the rate of vibration (the number of vibrations each second), e.g. of a wave

friction A force between surfaces, causing grip; also a drag force on something moving through air or liquid

galaxy A collection of millions of stars held together by gravity

gamma radiation A type of electromagnetic radiation with very short wavelength. It is emitted from atoms as a result of some radioactive changes

gravity A force between two masses. On Earth gravity causes things to be pulled towards the Earth; the force of gravity on an object is its weight. The pulling force of gravity between the Sun and a planet holds the planet in orbit around the Sun

hertz The unit of frequency, written as **Hz**

hydraulic system A mechanical system in which a force is passed through a liquid from one place to another

infra-red A type of electromagnetic radiation, with a wavelength longer than that of visible light. It causes a heating effect when absorbed

insulator (electrical) A material through which electric current cannot flow

insulator (of heat energy) A material through which the rate of conduction of energy is slow

ionising radiation Radiation that causes ionisation of atoms and molecules (leaving them positively or negatively charged), resulting in damage to living cells. Short-wavelength ultra-violet, X-rays, gamma rays, alpha and beta radiation are all ionising radiations

joule The unit of energy or work

longitudinal wave A wave in which the particles vibrate parallel to (in line with) the direction in which energy is transferred

magnetic field The space around a magnet in which magnetic material (iron and alloys containing iron) experiences forces

microwaves A type of electromagnetic radiation used for short-wave radio communications (e.g. those via satellites) and for cooking

newton The unit of force

non-renewable source A source of energy that, once used, cannot be used again, e.g. fossil fuels

ozone layer A layer of the atmosphere containing the gas ozone, which absorbs short-wavelength ultra-violet radiation

parallel circuit An electric circuit that has more than one loop; the parts in each loop can be switched on and off independently

pitch A note with a high pitch sounds 'high'; a note with a low pitch sounds 'low'

plastic A plastic material retains its new shape after being deformed

power The amount of work done each second, or the energy transferred each second

radiation Usually refers to energy transfer (e.g. heat) by electromagnetic waves; also the ionising emissions from radioactive substances, which may be electromagnetic waves or fast-moving particles

radioactivity The physical changes that take place inside atoms of radioactive substances, resulting in the emission of ionising radiation

reaction force An equal and opposite force exerted on an object at rest, e.g. an upward force balancing its weight

refraction The change in direction of a wave (e.g. light) as it passes from one material to another

renewable source A source of energy that can be used continually, e.g. the wind

resistance (electrical) Opposition to the flow of electric current. All parts of a circuit put up some resistance; the greater the resistance, the smaller the current

restoring force A force exerted by a deformed (e.g. stretched) object, tending to regain its original shape

series circuit An electric circuit in which all parts are connected in a single loop

sound wave A to-and-fro movement of air particles caused by a vibrating object

spectrum, electromagnetic The complete range of electromagnetic waves, grouped in order of wavelength/frequency, from radio waves (long wavelength, low frequency) to gamma radiation (short wavelength, high frequency)

spectrum of white light The 7 colours of the rainbow – red, orange, yellow, green, blue, indigo, violet – each of which has a slightly different wavelength

speed A measure of the distance covered by a moving object in unit time, e.g. 2 cm per second, 30 miles per hour

static electricity Unbalanced positive or negative electric charge

strength A measure of how well a material can withstand deforming forces

temperature A measure of how hot something is

tension A material is under tension if it is being stretched

transformer An electrical device that changes the voltage of an a.c. supply

transverse wave A wave in which the vibrations are at right angles to the direction in which energy is transferred

ultra-violet A type of electromagnetic radiation, with a wavelength shorter than that of visible light. It tans the skin but can cause damage to living tissue

ultrasound Sound with a frequency too high for humans to hear

volt The unit of voltage

voltage The voltage of an electrical supply is a measure of the power it can deliver to a particular circuit

watt The unit of power

wave A regular disturbance that carries energy away from a source

wavelength The distance occupied by one complete vibration of a wave

work Energy expended when a force acts on a moving object in the direction of, or opposite to, its motion

Index